HOMEMADE
FACIAL MASKS

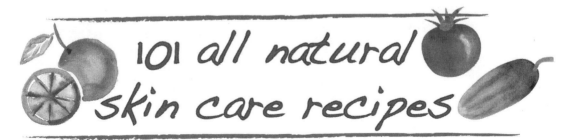

101 all natural skin care recipes

KRISTIN L. STEWART

Contents

Introduction

Who Is PrettySmart?

We know that untold fortunes are spent on slick magazine spreads and high budget commercials to persuade us that if we just buy their latest product, with the new breakthrough-scientific-space-age-polymer-stemcell-nanotechnology, we'll be instantly transformed into some version of the perfectly airbrushed model smiling back at us.

We know the ads are over the top—no anti-aging cream on the market is going to erase twenty-five years in five days.

We recognize the hype. So then why do the beauty industry giants (I call them, collectively, "Big Beauty") continue to speak so boldly and spend so much on all of those advertising campaigns?

Because they work—that's my best guess. And unlike drugs, skin care products are virtually unregulated by the FDA. Big Beauty therefore doesn't have to substantiate its claims. Maybe we've become numb to the hype. Or it's just so ubiquitous that the messages seep into our subconscious minds and lead our bodies (and our wallets) unthinkingly towards the most provocative promises of clear, glowing skin or anti-aging magic.

Women spend billions and billions of dollars every year on beauty products, including the ultra high-end anti-aging skin care formulas and cosmeceuticals. This, despite the lack of independent research and credible evidence to support most of Big Beauty's bold promises and audacious claims.

Do you really need all those products for your AM routine and all those other products for your PM routine to have clear, radiant skin? Probably not. We talk all about that and a whole lot more on the website— http://DIYBeautyTips.com. And when you visit the site, you can sign up for our newsletter, take advantage of the ever growing list of resources, look up skin care ingredients in the comprehensive ingredient dictionary, download newly added skin care recipes and facial treatments, and more. I want to personally invite you to join our community at DIYBeautyTips.com.

A Pleasure for Mind & Body

You are holding your one-stop source for homemade facial masks. And I hope it's even more than that. Because really, taking time to stop, breathe, and care for yourself is one of the most important things you can do for your whole self— mind, body and spirit.

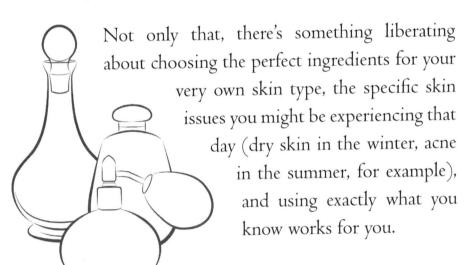

Not only that, there's something liberating about choosing the perfect ingredients for your very own skin type, the specific skin issues you might be experiencing that day (dry skin in the winter, acne in the summer, for example), and using exactly what you know works for you.

And isn't it empowering to actually know what ingredients you're spreading all over your face and body? I think so, yes—*empowering.*

When you make it in your own kitchen, you know for sure that you're only using fresh, natural ingredients—not some combination of mystery ingredients in the store-bought facial formulations on the shelves. Add to that the money you save by doing it yourself and it's easy to see why homemade facial masks and treatments are so well loved.

One of my favorite things about natural, homemade facial treatments is that they are so very nourishing—for your skin and body, of course, but also for your mind and spirit.

These recipes are simple, and most of them take just a little bit of time to formulate. Choose the perfect mask for how you're feeling in the moment, and then treat yourself to an all-natural, at-home spa experience — allow yourself to relax and be fully present in the moment. Let it be a meditation. However you do it, it's an excellent way to practice self-care and nurturing, and you deserve it.

In today's hurried world where stress and exhaustion take up too much of our lives, do-it-yourself at home skin, hair and body treatments are a creative, enriching and inexpensive way to slow down, center, and connect with what's important.

Enjoy. And please, share these recipes with friends and family. Giggle with girlfriends as you luxuriate together in your very own at-home spa. Have you ever smeared kitty litter all over your face with a friend (I mean on purpose)? It's a recipe for fun, I assure you (but please be sure to read the whole recipe before you attempt these "speciality masks")!

Or perhaps you're in the mood to invite a more intimate connection by sharing some of the more sensual, delicious recipes. Chocolate, anyone? However you're feeling, doing a mask at home can soothe your skin and nourish your mind, spirit and even your relationships. You can find more information, suggestions and do-it-yourself beauty tips at DIYBeautyTips.com.

A Luxury Spa In Your Kitchen & Bath

You have all the makings of your very own luxury spa right in your kitchen and bath. With the help of the recipes and tips in this book, you'll discover a whole world of natural relaxation and rejuvenation aids already waiting for you in your cabinets. And anything you don't happen to have on hand you can find easily enough on your next trip to the grocery store.

Once you've tried a few of the tested recipes and you're comfortable with how your particular skin reacts to the various ingredients, you can start experimenting with those components and making your own unique formulations. Different ingredients allow you to target your specific problem areas and skin type simply by adding unique combinations of some basic natural ingredients to your homemade facial routine.

In addition to the money you'll save and the convenience of treating yourself to a home spa experience, homemade facial masks are often better for your skin than their store-bought counterparts. Plus, making your own facial mask is pretty easy,

PrettySmart Tip

Here's a simple, natural recipe that works wonders for skin that's both oily and sensitive. After cleansing with water (just water), apply organic, full fat yogurt to your skin; leave it on for about 10 minutes before rinsing with warm (not hot) water.

Your skin should look and feel clean, smooth and radiant. The lactic acid in the yogurt acts as a mild exfoliant but shouldn't cause irritation.

especially with these homemade facial mask recipes. There are over 100 facial masks and natural skin care tips in this book for you to experiment with. Relax and have fun with these recipes. In no time, your skin will be glowing and you'll feel fabulous.

Start with the recipes and ingredients suggested for your skin type. Avoid any ingredients that you may be allergic to. It's always a good idea to test any new skin care formulas (whether you make it at home or purchase products) by using them as directed on the back of your ear before applying them to your face. Wait for a few minutes and check to be sure you're not experiencing any irritation or redness where you applied your test sample.

Always be especially careful applying any formulas around your eyes, as that skin is especially sensitive, and as a general rule you do not want to get any product too close to (or inside of) your eyes.

As you play with different recipes, notice which ingredients and combinations lead to improvements in the overall health and complexion of your skin. There is a Notes section for each recipe, and a Face Mask Journal towards the end of the book so you can jot down your observations and capture any special combinations you particularly enjoy.

Skin Care 101

First, Do No Harm! That is the cardinal rule of skin care. It may seem obvious, but it's worth taking a few minutes to remember. This may surprise you: Many visible signs of skin damage are the result of harmful external factors rather than, say, the normal aging process.

Really, the easiest, cheapest and most effective step you can take when it comes to your skin care strategy is to *minimize avoidable external damage.*

Easy enough, right?

The first step to avoiding skin damage is to understand the likely causes, so let's talk about some of the most important factors that could be causing damage to your skin.

Keep in mind, too, that skin damage does not always cause pain or even visible irritation, so you want to be aware of negative factors that could be accumulating at low levels unnoticed. Here is a summary of the most common causes of skin damage, and how to avoid them.

Ultraviolet Radiation

We all know that UV rays from the sun and tanning beds contribute to wrinkles and skin aging, and they increase our risk for skin cancer. What you may not know is that many sunscreens do not adequately protect your skin, some may actually cause damage, and staying out of direct sunlight will only partially protect you from sun damage.

Here's a twist to the typical "wear SPF 30+ everyday" mantra: Most sunscreens on the market have the potential to actually CAUSE free radical skin damage when you wear them in the sunlight. Yes, astounding! But unfortunately, also true. (For more about sunscreen, including a list of potentially harmful sunscreens, related research, and suggestions for the most beneficial sunscreens, visit DIYBeautyTips.com). Add to that the fact that lots of people are talking about the health *benefits* of being out in the sun for some period of time. Researchers are finding that many of us are deficient in Vitamin D—a vitamin that has a greater impact on health and wellness than doctors and scientists previously realized—and sun exposure is one of the most effective ways that we get Vitamin D.

Still, studies tell us that between 70% and 90% of all skin damage is caused by UV exposure. And skin cancer *is* a big deal: it can be quick, quiet and deadly.

So what's the answer? Like most things in life, it isn't as simple as we might like it to be. But here's something to consider: Dermatologists recommend mineral sunscreens that use titanium dioxide and zinc oxide, which are called "physical" sunscreens because they sort of perch on the surface of the skin. These are in contrast to chemical sunscreens, which contain substances that may be absorbed by the skin (and many of which, research has found, are harmful and can cause further damage to your skin).

Sun avoidance, especially during peak hours, as well as protective clothing, sunglasses, proven antioxidant supplementation externally and internally (from a healthy diet) are all at least as important as good sunscreens if you want to avoid damage from those UV rays.

Harsh Detergents

Harsh detergents, particularly those called "ionic detergents," may also be harmful to your skin. They are called ionic because their molecules become charged when dissolved in water. They are what make the sudsy lather in your shampoo. The most common and ubiquitous ionic detergents are sodium

PrettySmart Tip

Harsh detergents are for cleaning greasy pots and pans, not your delicate skin.

lauryl sulfate, sodium laureth sulfate (both use the acronym SLS) and their analogs, like ammonium lauryl sulfate, ammonium laureth sulfate and others.

In fact, SLS is often used to produce experimental skin damage in clinical studies of skin protectors. Because they are such powerful detergents, SLS and analogs are widely used in household and body care products like shampoos, soaps, dishwashing liquids, laundry detergents, and so on.

Unlike the sunscreen discussion, there is no "on the other hand" here. There is nothing about SLS you need (and once you break your addiction to that thick lathery goodness we all got used to growing up, you'll never miss it!).

Read the ingredient list on all products that come into contact with your skin or scalp. If they contain ionic detergents, eliminate or minimize such contact by using similar products with nonionic detergents, alternative cleansing methods, wearing gloves when washing dishes, etc. For example, if your shampoo or soap has SLS or its analogs, you can switch to a non-irritating SLS-free shampoo, or stop using "shampoo" altogether and cleanse your hair using the "conditioner-only" cleansing method (abbreviated "co" or "co-washing" on some of the hair care forums online). Also, trade in your harsh soap for a glycerin-based moisturizing soap.

Chlorine and Hot Water

If you're anything like me, you love a long hot shower. So it pains me to have to tell you this... you may love it, but your skin—well, not so much.

The chlorine in our tap water is an oxidative agent; that's great to kill bacteria, but not so great for our skin because it may actually cause some skin damage. And here's the kicker: The hotter the water, the greater the damage, because the rate of chemical reaction increases with temperature. At the same time, you also don't want to exposure skin to water that's too cold (certainly not icy cold water), because it too has the potential to cause damage for other reasons.

> **PrettySmart Tip**
>
> Avoid exposing your skin to water that is too hot or very cold. Tepid to warm water is best to avoid skin damage.

Limit baths and showers to once a day or less, and try not to soak in a hot tub for too long. At least make it warm, not hot.

Skin Irritants

Anything that irritates can cause skin damage in a couple of ways. First, it may directly damage your skin matrix and cells. Second, it can trigger an inflammatory or allergic reaction in the skin, which can then cause skin damage by the release of destructive free radicals and what's called metalloproteinanses or MMP (these are the enzymes that degrade the skin matrix, shredding your beloved collagen and elastin).

Actually, the damage that's caused by the skin's reaction to whatever causes the irritation is often much greater then the damage caused by the irritant itself! This is particularly true for those of us with sensitive skin, because our skin develops inflammatory and/or allergic reactions in response to even mild irritants. And that's why we should try to avoid skin irritants. Those of us with sensitive skin should be especially careful.

Inflammation & Acne

Generally speaking, inflammation is a reaction of the body in response to various types of damage like infection, trauma, abrasions, burns, etc. It's not that it is in and of itself bad for you—inflammation is an important and necessary part of our body's healing process. But prolonged or excessive inflammation is damaging to the skin (or any other organ where it occurs). What happens is this: Inflammation causes a release of large amounts of damaging free radicals and MMP, which, among other things, speeds up the aging process. While occasional short-term and self-limiting inflammation from cuts, or abrasions (or even cosmetic procedures) are probably not a major concern, chronic inflammation is something you definitely want to deal with.

PrettySmart Tip

Be gentle and avoid irritation. Irritation and inflammation are very, very bad for your skin. Very. Bad. Clear?

Irritation can result from unprotected sun exposure, washing your face with water that is too hot, using skin care products that contain irritating ingredients including SLS, SD alchohol, menthol, ammonia and many more (for a list of irritants to avoid visit the Resources section online at DIYBeautyTips.com). Irritation can also result from over-cleansing, scrubbing too vigorously, exfoliating too often, or overusing makeup and skin care products. This impairs your skin's immune system as well as its protective outer layer, and causes collagen breakdown. If you have oily skin or trouble with acne, irritation triggers nerve endings inside skin pores, which activates androgen production—the hormone that makes pores bigger and increases oil production. None of it is good for oily skin (or for any skin type).

Acne is more than a cosmetic issue—it is the most common cause of skin inflammation. That's why it's important to treat chronic acne. The problem is that a lot of acne treatments can cause more problems than they solve. For example, products that contain benzoyl peroxide are irritants and can themselves cause skin damage if used improperly or excessively. Treatment should never cause more damage then the issue you're treating!

If you are battling acne, remember that stronger, harsher, stingy-er stuff isn't a good idea—that will only work against you.

In addition to acne, other common skin conditions causing chronic inflammation include eczema, psoriasis, dermatitis and inflammatory forms of rosacea. Consult your dermatologist to find an effective but nonirritating (or at least minimally irritating) treatment that is best for you. And try some of the homemade facial mask recipes in this book specifically noted as gentle and for skin prone to acne.

Eye Puffiness

Puffiness in the eye area results from what is called mild facial edema. Edema is just the excess fluid accumulation in soft tissue that happens with swelling. The main problem with edema is that the swelling stretches the skin and eventually leads to wrinkles and sagging.

The skin around your eyes is particularly prone to edema because of the dense capillary network around your eyes and the lack of fat padding. Morning puffiness is a common situation that can be exacerbated by lack of sleep, alcohol consumption, and other lifestyle factors. And here's the worst part: Morning eye puffiness is one of the biggest contributors to the aging of the skin around our eyes. Ready to battle that puffiness now?

What's with the skin around our eyes, anyway? For one thing, it is different from the rest of your skin: It has almost no sebaceous glands (which makes it really prone to dryness), and it is thinner and more sensitive than the rest of the skin on your face. That skin is also stressed by all the eye movements and squinting that are part of our natural facial expressions.

Here are some things you can do to reduce eye puffiness:

- Sleep on your back (believe it or not, it keeps the blood pressure in your facial vessels down);

- Avoid too many fluids late in the evening;

- Limit your sodium intake so that you do not increase water retention in your body (and thus, edema);

- Avoid alcohol (it encourages the accumulation of fluid in extracellular space); and

- Get enough sleep (this is good for all kinds of things, including eye puffiness).

If you find yourself waking up with puffy eyes, you can quickly reduce eye puffiness and thus minimize its damaging effects on your skin. Here are some ways to do that:

- Cool your face down by exposing it to cool air or a cold washcloth for 10-15 minutes. If you use ice or any sort of frozen pack be sure it's not too cold (wrap a towel around it) and hold it to your face for less than 30 seconds at a time, then rest, and don't exceed five minutes total.

- Another quick trick that works wonders is to apply a small amount of hemorrhoid cream to the areas that are puffy. (Hey, there's a reason some of these tips are "secrets," right?). The cream contains a blood vessel constrictor called phenylephrine. Don't use it more than twice a week, and use only a small amount. If you experience headache stop using it immediately.

- A cool tea bag compress is another solution. Place two tea bags in warm water, steep for a few seconds, remove the bags and place them in the refrigerator for about a half hour. Lay back and place the cool, moist tea bags on closed eyes for 10-20 minutes. Tea polyphenols act as an astringent, tightening the skin, while caffeine promotes drainage of fluid from extracellular space.

Overuse of Makeup & Skin Care Products

Makeup products can also contain skin irritants. Be sure you monitor how your makeup affects your skin and use makeup in moderation, particularly on the skin around your eyes. Long-lasting makeup may be particularly harmful because it tends to contain harsher chemicals and also requires highly irritating solvents for its removal. Go easy.

Consider cutting back on using too many skin care products. There's good reason—many products are simply ineffective. I'm talking specifically about skin treatments, "cosmeceuticals," or other products containing active ingredients meant to improve your skin. And here's the real problem: Many products are more than just a waste of money; they may actually prevent optimal absorption of any truly effective treatment contained in the products you're using. Moreover, some products actually contain ingredients with the potential for low-level, long-term skin damage. And then some products with scientifically proven benefits for skin (retinoids, vitamin C and alpha-hydroxy acids, for example), may cause skin irritation—even skin damage—if overused or misused. This is not the place to talk too much about such things, but I wanted to at least mention it. Be very selective about what products you use on your skin.

Feeling extra sassy? Join me at DIYBeautyTips.com to learn about compounding your own scientifically proven, skin rejuvenating creams, lotions and serums using only proven, active ingredients—that's the best way to know exactly what and how much you're using, and that it's fresh (not past its shelf life and thus totally ineffective).

Too Much Cleansing & Exfoliation

Some skin care routines may do more harm then good when overused, like too much cleansing and/or exfoliating. Excessive cleansing strips the skin of its protective sebum and can lead to dryness, skin sensitivity and other problems. Avoid cleansing with harsh detergents and alcohol-based solutions. And don't wash your skin with water that's too hot. Use a gentle cleanser and stick to washing your skin no more than twice a day.

If you're going to exfoliate—which I love to do—be sure you don't do it too often or too aggressively. Occasional exfoliation is refreshing, increases circulation and brightens your skin's appearance. But limit it to twice a week, max, and be *gentle*—else you risk doing damage to living cells, which, if continued, can harm your skin's long-term capacity to regenerate.

Optimize for Your Skin Condition Now

Skin care and homemade facial masks ought to be adjusted to fit your current condition. Keep in mind that your "skin type" may change with the season, your diet, your environment, and your age. For many of us, our skin tends to be oilier in the summer and drier in the winter. Menopause often brings about a change from oily or normal to dry skin. On the other hand, a shift from a low-fat diet to that rich in certain fats (particularly essential fatty acids) may turn dry skin to normal.

Consider your skin condition before you decide on your facial mask recipe. That's what so fabulous about having a bunch of recipes at your fingertips—there are so many delicious, luxurious face mask recipes to choose from; as you do, rely on your mood, what's in your kitchen at the moment, and your skin type and condition that day.

Skin Types & Kitchen Ingredients

Here are just some of the many ingredients you can use to pamper your skin at home.

FOR DRY SKIN	
Avocado	Moisturizing; Vitamins A and E provide essential antioxidants
Bran	Tightens large pores; combats dryness
Coconut Milk	Essential fatty acids provide moisture
Egg Yolk	Conditions skin (save the whites for normal and oily skin types)

Elderberry Blossom	Moisturizes dry skin
Honey	Antiseptic and antibacterial properties; refines pores; tightens skin; anti-blemish; anti-wrinkle
Mayonnaise	Cleans; moisturizes
Oatmeal	An effective exfoliant leaving your skin glowing while enhancing tone and texture; soothing; healing; relieves itching
Olive Oil	Contains vitamin E and antioxidants
Peach	Vitamins A and C tighten skin and open up pores without overly drying skin
Sunflower Seed Oil	Contains vitamins A and D and essential fatty acids
Sweet Almond Oil	Fatty acids help with inflamed skin, restoring moisture while healing and soothing

For Oily Skin & Skin Prone to Acne

Apple	Contains vitamins A and C that help to exfoliate the skin
Arrowroot	Dries up blemishes
Barley	Anti-blemish; refines pores; retards wrinkles
Citrus Fruits	Vitamin C; astringent
Cucumber	Natural toning astringent; reduces under-eye puffiness
Safflower, Sunflower, Sesame, Meadowfoam, and Jojoba	These are some of the oils that are good for oily skin
Egg White	Conditions (save the yolk for dry skin); draws out oil leaving skin toned and tightened immediately after use
Sage	Good toner for oily skin

Tomato	Mild levels of acidity to help remove excess oil; unclogs pores

All Skin Types

Apple Cider Vinegar	Said to contain many untold healing properties; helps to balance pH of skin; reduces redness; reduces blemishes; soothes itchy and sunburned skin
Banana & Banana Peel	Contains lutein (an antioxidant) and potassium
Carrot	Antioxidants and antiseptic properties; sloughs ; moisturizes
Castor Oil	Very cleansing oil; may relieve itching; fades brown spots; nice eyelash treatment
Chamomile	Tones all types of complexions
Cocoa Powder	High levels of vitamins and antioxidants
Cornmeal	Refines pores

Epsom Salt	Anti-blemish
Grapefruit	Tightens large pores
Herbs like Rosemary, Sage, and Fennel	Help to cleanse and tone skin
Lavender	Soothes
Milk (including whole, skim, buttermilk, cream, and sour cream)	Refines pores, soothes all skin types; cools sunburn
Papaya	Gentle exfoliant containing antibacterial properties
Pineapple	Cleans and tones
Pumpkin	Vitamins A, C, and E to help renew and soften skin
Strawberry	Contain an exfoliating acid that helps to cleanse and tone the skin

Yogurt

Exfoliating acids leave skin hydrated without over drying

Homemade Facial Masks

Preparation & Tools

Here is a list of recommended tools you can use to make the facial mask recipes in this book. All you really need is probably in your kitchen right now! And remember, there are no hard rules with regard to equipment—just use whatever works for you.

Blender or food processor. It's handy to use a blender or food processor to quickly whip together your ingredients. A food processor is usually easier to use for grinding oatmeal, almonds and other seeds. A coffee grinder is another great alternative for grinding up nuts and oatmeal. Or you can go old school and use a mortar and pestle.

Bowls. Most of these recipes require a small or medium sized bowl, but it's a good idea to have a variety of sizes of bowls around. Whether you choose glass, enamel, stainless steel, ceramic or plastic is up to you.

Cheesecloth, coffee filters and a wire strainer. If you do anything with loose tea leaves or herbs, you'll want to drain the liquid and discard the herbs before using the solution in your mask. I find coffee filters are better for super-watery liquids, and cheesecloth is great for most everything else. (Coffee filter tip: place filter inside a strainer before purring your liquid through it). Don't have cheesecloth? Grab some nylon stockings and you've got a darn good substitute.

Cutting board, basic cooking utensils and measuring cups/spoons. 'nuff said.

Double boiler. Basically, a double boiler is just one pan set inside another pan of a similar size. When you heat the water in the bottom pan then place the second pan inside, it provides a gentle, even, low heat and you avoid having to worry about scorching whatever is in that second pan. When you're making something with fatty ingredients like oil, waxes or butters, you need to pay close attention to keeping the heat low. If you overheat, boil or scorch those ingredients, consider them ruined! But for these facial mask recipes you will be heating few items—like honey and water (and you can even use the microwave for that if you like). Frankly, I hate to clean up and will avoid using extra pans whenever possible, so I usually just use a basic stainless pan on a low heat setting and make sure to stir occasionally.

Facial brush. You can purchase a cosmetics brush especially made for applying facials, or use a medium size makeup brush you already have. Just be sure you've cleaned it before use (wash with regular hand soap and let dry).

Mortar and pestle. This is handy to have in the kitchen—especially for mashing berries and fruits. You can use them to crush seeds and fresh cut herbs as well. If you don't have a mortar and pestle, use a wide bowl and the back of a spoon for something that needs mashing.

Make a Clean Start

Before using any tools to make your facial mask, you need to be sure your workspace and supplies are clean and sanitized. This is doubly important when you're making products that you'll be storing and using on a regular basis, but it's good practice for your facial masks as well. You want to be sure everything you're using is free from harmful germs, bacteria, mold and fungus. Never underestimate the importance of this first step.

You can kill the bad germs and bacteria on your counters by wiping them down with commercial sanitizer, alcohol, or—if green is your color—white distilled vinegar. There are many ways to sterilize your tools and workspace, but the simplest and safest way I know of is with regular alcohol from the drugstore and a cloth (or some gauze). Just saturate the cloth or gauze, wipe it over whatever you want to sanitize, and let it air dry. Keeping a spray bottle full of alcohol is handy for cleaning utensils, whisks and such.

Other inexpensive and effective sanitizers include hydrogen peroxide (at 3% it's strong enough to kill most types of bacteria in less than 15 minutes) and a bleach-water solution. If you want to use bleach for sanitizing everything, add 1 tablespoon of bleach to 1 gallon of water and soak your equipment in the bleach-water solution for about 20 minutes. After that, drain everything and let it air dry. (There is no need to rinse at that concentration).

PrettySmart Tip

A Note About Sanitizing: When you're particularly concerned about sanitizing bottles and jars (for using with skin care products), consider using hydrogen peroxide to rinse your sanitized items after wiping them down with alcohol. Water actually has all kinds of contaminants that could breed bacteria and other stuff, so using that after the alcohol can sort of defeat the purpose unless you boil it first and let it cool. That's probably not necessary when preparing these homemade facial masks because you will be using them immediately or very soon after you've made them. But when you want to compound your own active skin care serums, lotions and creams, you will want to pay special attention to such things.

More information, bonus recipes, and skin care tips are on the website: DIYBeautyTips.com. There you can join the

PrettySmart community, sign up for our newsletter, and learn about compounding your own active ingredient skin care serums and creams!

Keep In Mind...

Essential Oils

There are several recipes in the book that call for essential oils. These are very potent oils typically sold in small 5 and 15 ml bottles because you only use 1-3 drops at a time. By the way, these "oils" don't feel the least bit oily and they soak completely into the skin.

I recommend you use only pure, therapeutic-grade essential oils in these recipes (if not, simply leave them out of your facial mask recipe). Unfortunately, these are more costly than most essential oils. But most essential oils are produced using high temperatures, rapid processing and chemical solvents during the distillation process; and while they may smell just as good as the pure, high-quality oils, they will lack any real therapeutic benefits and could potentially be harmful. Even when using the very best essential oils, be careful; if they are not on the recipe list, consult with someone knowledgeable about how, when and which essential oils to use before you incorporate them into any personal care routine.

The oils in this recipe were chosen specifically because of their therapeutic value—not because of how they smell. The good news is, even though the high grade oils are more expensive, they have some amazing benefits and you can use them for a lot more than just your homemade facial mask recipes. They are powerful antioxidants; their small molecular size means they quickly penetrate skin; they are lipid soluble so they penetrate cell walls; they are regenerating, and oxygenating. Depending on the oil, they can be antibacterial, antifungal, antimicrobial, antiparasitic, antiviral, and antiseptic. Those that I've chosen for these recipes are particularly well suited to skin care. But again, please use only the highest grade essential oils or simply leave them out of the mask recipe altogether. (I currently use Young Living essential oils, but they are not the only high quality oils available.)

Honey

Many of the recipes also call for honey. Some of the recipes call specifically for warm honey. That is primarily because cold or room temperature honey can be very thick. Any time a recipe calls for honey, whether or not the recipe specifically says so, you may want to warm the honey a little (on the stove or in the microwave is fine)—just until it becomes a thinner, more runny consistency. I find mixing ingredients is always easier when the honey is warm and runny.

Always Avoid Eyes and Area Around the Eyes

In all cases, please be careful to keep the mask away from your eyes and the skin around your eyes. When a recipe calls for lemon, lime, orange or other citrus juice, I often remind you to be careful to avoid your eye area because the citrus can cause extra stinging and irritation to the skin around the eyes. But the same is true for all of the recipes—always avoid the area around your eyes.

Clays & Kitty Litter

You will find a few clay-based mask recipes in this book, and some of them actually tell you about how some people use kitty litter for their facial mask. Clay masks are wonderful and have been around for eons. But kitty litter? "Are you crazy?!" Actually, maybe it's surprising, but not exactly crazy—this is, apparently, one of those "secret" beauty tips I've come across a couple of times in my travels. I'm not going to recommend for or against, but because some suggest it makes for an uber-cheap-and-fabulous clay mask, I wanted to at least pass it on.

If you're up for it, be sure you use ONLY the 100% natural, unscented litter with zero additives. Here is what's not-so-crazy about it: the stuff is bentonite clay—the very same ingredient many high priced spas use to make their muds and special clays for their face and body treatments. Not only that, bentonite clay (also called montmorillonite) is an edible clay from naturally occurring volcanic ash sediments, and contains over 70 trace minerals, and it is one of the most effective and powerful healing clays used to treat both internal and external maladies. It is traditionally used as an internal supplement to assist with mineral deficiencies, and to help bind toxins making them more soluble. Externally, bentonite is used as a clay poultice, mud pack, in the bath, and in skin care recipes as it has the ability to absorb toxins, impurities, heavy metals and other contaminants from the body.

However, there are a couple of types of bentonite clay: sodium bentonite and calcium bentonite. Most of the kitty litters in the US, as best I can tell, are made up of sodium bentonite, and some claim that sodium bentonite is a low-level carcinogen. Calcium bentonite seems to be safer, and I did manage to find a few cat litters are made from it (but it required quite a search). I found one in my local health food co-op, but the litter was more expensive than just buying the food-grade powder on the next isle over, so that kind of defeated the whole purpose!

If you decide to be adventurous and actually use kitty litter for your clay mask, let me emphasize, again, that you should only use 100% natural, unscented, clay litter. You can use it straight from the bag, but the litter is made up of bentonite granules, which are much larger particles than those in cosmetic clay powder. The bigger particles are more difficult to mix into a lovely mask, so I recommend you pulverize the kitty litter with a coffee grinder or food processor before using it.

Now, if smearing kitty litter on your face doesn't appeal to you, I understand. I love the idea of a savvy, cost-effective alternative to expensive beauty treatments. And yes, I tried the kitty litter mask. But full disclosure: In the future, I'm going to stick with cosmetic clay powders, at least until I have a better understanding of all the ins and outs of the kitty-litter-bentonite-issues.

Cosmetic clays are natural facial wonders: they cleanse, invigorate and heal. There are several kinds of clays, each with properties that might work best for your skin type and condition. All clays, however, share properties of absorption, which allow them to draw out impurities and toxins from the skin. Rich in trace minerals, clays invigorate and brighten skin by stimulating circulation. They also gently exfoliate skin, ridding it of debris and dead skin cells.

Here are some clay mask basics. To make a thick paste, you generally begin by using 2 tablespoons of clay to 1-2 tablespoons of water (distilled water is best). Other ways to make the paste, which you will see in several of the recipes here, is to substitute plain, full-fat yogurt for the water, or skin-friendly oils such as jojoba oil.

- If your mixture is too dry, add more liquid until a nice, thick mud is formed. Then spread a thick layer on your face.

- Leave on for 10-15 minutes (it can be too drying to leave on for longer than that).

- Do not allow the mask to fully dry on your face. To prevent it drying up, apply a thick layer, and keep a spray bottle with (distilled) water nearby to mist your face as you relax and enjoy your mask.

- Gently rinse the mask off with tepid-warm water and pat dry.

- It's always a good idea to moisturize after finishing your facial mask.

- As a general rule, use a clay mask no more than once per week.

Common Cosmetic Clays

Green. Green clay is very absorbent and it disinfects and heals the skin by drawing out toxins and impurities. Cosmetically, green clay is admired for its ability to stimulate blood and lymph circulation, remove dead skin cells, absorb impurities and fats, and tone and strengthen connective tissues. After using it, skin feels fresh, smooth, radiant, and soft. Green clay is also fabulous for helping to clear problem skin areas, and is gentle enough to use weekly, or even daily on acne breakout spots. Avoid green clay if you have dry, irritated or sensitive skin as it can be drying.

Yellow. Yellow clay is also cleansing, but it is gentler than green clay. Yellow has more iron than any other clay. It is mineral-rich, revitalizing and tones skin nicely. It's best for oily and mixed skin types, and also good for tired, dull skin or mature skin.

Red. Red clay is cleansing, but gentler than the green and yellow. Heals breaking capillaries. Red is for normal to dry skin; it's also good for dull skin, delicate skin and those with skin conditions like rosacea.

White (also called Kaolin Clay). White clay is the lightest and most delicate clay. White clay is made up of fine clay particles, and has a lightweight, fluffy consistency. This clay is more widely used than any other cosmetic clay, and is frequently found in powders, body packs, skin care products, deodorants, soaps, scrubs, poultices, cosmetics, facial masks, and toiletries. White clay will gently draw impurities from the skin without removing natural oils and at the same time exfoliate, cleanse, and stimulate circulation. White clay is suitable for all skin types—oily, blemish prone, normal, sensitive, dry, or mature skin.

Pink. Pink clay is a mixture of ⅔ red and ⅓ white clay. It has the cleansing properties of red clay, but is much gentler thanks to the white clay. It strengthens the skin by stimulating circulation, at the same time soothing

> ### *PrettySmart Tip*
>
> Pink clay is a great alternative to red and white clay, and you can make pink clay yourself by combining ⅔ red with ⅓ white. Aside from pink clay, however, mixing clays is not recommended.

it. Pink clay is a great choice for sensitive and delicate skin, rough skin, and skin conditions like rosacea.

Apple Refresher

A refreshing blend of apple and honey for skin that is oily and prone to acne.

INGREDIENTS

1 apple
6 tablespoons honey

1 Warm honey to a runny consistency.

2 Peel and chop apple into small pieces; mash with mortar and pestle, grind up in blender, or smash with the back of a spoon. (If apple is too hard or crisp, you can boil it for a few minutes and it will soften up.)

3 In a medium bowl, mix honey and apple mash together.

4 Apply evenly to clean face; relax and leave on for 10-15 minutes.

5 Rinse with warm water and pat dry.

Apple and Cucumber Classic

This mask is a classic and will leave your skin feeling clean and refreshed.

INGREDIENTS

1 cucumber
½ medium apple
1 egg white
1 teaspoon lemon juice
1 teaspoon lime juice

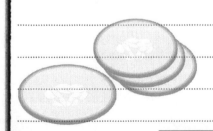

Notes:

Homemade Facial Masks

1 Peel cucumber and apple and cut them into small chunks.

2 To a blender or food processor, add cucumber, apple, egg white, lemon and lime juice; blend well.

3 Apply mixture to face and neck, taking special care to avoid the eye area.

 4 Relax and leave on for 30 minutes; rinse with warm water and pat dry.

Secret Brew for Trouble Spots

This facial recipe is for use as a spot treatment on areas of breakouts and inflammation.
It is not meant to be used as an all over mask.

INGREDIENTS

1 teaspoon of brewer's yeast
3 tablespoons plain, full-fat yogurt

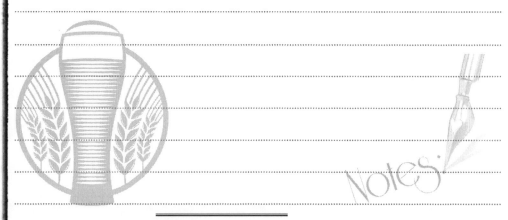

Notes:

1 In a medium bowl, mix yeast with the yogurt.

2 Use the mixture as a spot treatment only on acne breakouts or other trouble spots on your face (not your entire face).

3 Allow mixture to sit for about 15 minutes; rinse with warm water and pat dry.

Carrots & Honey

A lovely mask for normal to oily skin.

INGREDIENTS

2-3 large carrots; cooked and mashed
4½ tablespoons honey, warm

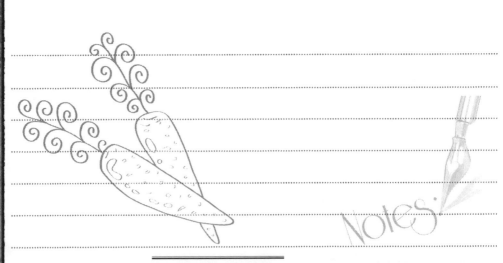

Notes:

1 Warm honey to a runny consistency.

2 Add carrots to boiling water and cook until soft; let carrots cool.

3 Using a hand mixer or a blender, mix carrots and honey to a thick paste.

4 Apply to freshly cleaned face (do not massage into skin); relax and leave on for 10 to 15 minutes.

5 Rinse with warm water and pat dry.

Egg Whites & Lemon

If you have oily skin you'll love how well this
mask cleans pores and gets rid of blackheads.

INGREDIENTS

2 egg whites
1 teaspoon lemon juice

Notes:

1 In a medium bowl combine lemon juice and egg whites.

2 Beat together until fluffy.

3 With a facial brush, apply mixture evenly to face and neck, taking care to avoid the area near your eyes.

4 Relax and leave on for 15 minutes; rinse with warm water and pat dry.

Grapefruit Facial Mask

This facial mask is particularly
well suited for oily skin.

INGREDIENTS

1 teaspoon grapefruit juice
1 teaspoon sour cream
1 egg white

Notes:

Homemade Facial Masks

1 In a small bowl combine sour cream, egg white and grapefruit juice together and mix well.

2 Apply mixture with facial brush, paying special attention to oily parts of the skin.

 3 Allow mask to sit for about 10 minutes; rinse with warm water and pat dry.

Lemon Lime Fizzy Time

Clear your pores with this mega cleansing mask
with a little extra fizz.

INGREDIENTS

¾ cup plain, full-fat yogurt
2 teaspoons lemon juice
2 teaspoons lime juice
Splash of club soda

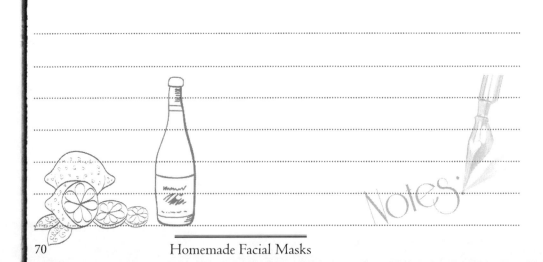

Notes:

1 In a large bowl mix lemon and lime juice with yogurt.

2 Apply mixture evenly to your face and neck, taking special care to avoid the eye area.

3 Leave on for 15 minutes as you breathe deeply and relax.

4 Now the fun part: Rinse with a big splash or two of club soda, and feel the fizz boost your skin's circulation!

For Oily Skin

Lemon Tomato Blackhead Buster

The acids in the tomato and lemon work wonders on acne and blackheads.

INGREDIENTS

1 over-ripe tomato
1 teaspoon lemon juice
1 teaspoon dry oatmeal

1 Cut the tomato in half, scoop the meat out and place into blender.

2 Add lemon and oatmeal; blend to a puree.

 3 Apply to the face and neck, with extra care to avoid eye area.

4 Relax and let it sit for 20 minutes; rinse with warm water and pat dry.

Strawberries & Yogurt

This is a simple and delicious mask that's a treat for your skin (and your tummy too, so may want to make a little extra).

INGREDIENTS

4-6 strawberries
1 tablespoon plain, full-fat yogurt

Notes:

1 In a medium bowl, use the back of a large spoon to mash strawberries.

2 Add yogurt to mashed strawberries and mix well.

3 Apply to the face and neck, with care to avoid eye area; relax and let it sit for 10 minutes.

4 Rinse with warm water and pat dry.

Clarity Mask

To cleanse and clarify oily skin.

INGREDIENTS

1 teaspoon lemon juice
2 egg whites
4 teaspoons honey
1 cup strawberries

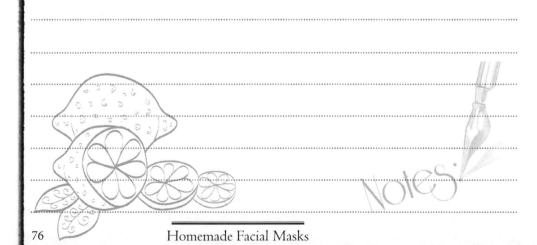

Notes:

1 Blend strawberries, honey, egg whites and lemon juice together with a blender or food processor.

2 Apply mask to freshly cleaned face; relax and leave on for 10 minutes.

3 Rinse with warm water and pat dry.

For Oily Skin

Tomato Potato Flour Cleansing Mask

The gentle acid in tomatoes will cleanse and tighten pores.

INGREDIENTS

1 tomato
2-3 tablespoons potato flour

Notes:

1 Peel the flesh of one tomato away from the skin and chop into several pieces; discard skin.

2 In a small bowl, mix tomato with potato flour to form a paste. (Add more potato flour if paste is too runny.)

3 Apply mixture evenly to face and neck, with extra care to avoid eye area; relax and let it sit for 20 minutes.

4 Rinse with warm water and pat dry.

The Aspirin Mask

Aspirin is actually a form of Beta Hydroxy Acid (or BHA), which is found in many skin creams. It works by gently exfoliating the skin. Over time, BHA's can help clarify skin tone and promote healing of blemishes.

NOTE: Do not use if allergic to aspirin.

INGREDIENTS

6-10 tablets plain, uncoated aspirin
½ teaspoon plain yogurt
½ teaspoon honey

Optional:
¼ teaspoon tea tree oil

Notes:

1 Begin by dissolving uncoated aspirin tablets in hot water (add a few drops of water at a time — just enough to get the aspirin soft).

2 Mash the soggy aspirin tablets together with a mortar and pestle (or just use a spoon!).

3 Mix yogurt and honey together (and tea tree oil if you have a breakout or oily skin issues), then add the aspirin mash and mix well.

4 Apply mask to clean face and leave on for 5-10 minutes. Rinse well.

PrettySmart Tip

Be sure you use uncoated, dissolvable tablets.

Do not use Tylenol, Motrin or other pain relievers—(they are not made of the same thing).

Oily Skin

Acne Tonic with Basil

This is a very wet facial, so be sure to wear a
towel around your neck as you apply it.

INGREDIENTS

3 leaves fresh basil (or 3 teaspoons
of dried basil leaves)
1 cup water

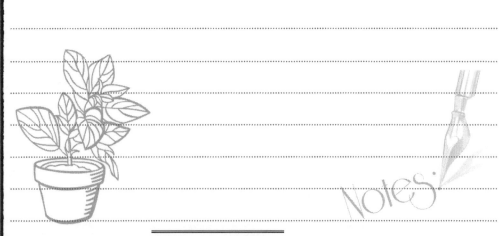

Notes:

1 Heat water to almost a boil, remove from heat, and add basil to steep for 15 minutes.

2 Drape a towel around your neck.

3 When cool, apply the facial tonic to your face and neck with a cotton ball.

4 Relax and leave on for 25 minutes; rinse with cool water and pat dry.

Balancing Beauty Mask

Try this mask if you're having any problems with your skin like acne or rosacea. The fat in the cream plus the salt helps to heal, while the flour thickens the mask.

INGREDIENTS

1 teaspoon garbanzo bean flour
1 tablespoon whipping cream
2 teaspoons distilled water
1 pinch of fine grain salt

Notes:

1 In a small bowl mix together flour, whipping cream, water and salt.

2 Apply mixture evenly to face and neck; relax and let sit for about 15 minutes.

3 Rinse with warm water and pat dry.

Banana Acne Buster

This banana mask recipe is great for
helping acne-prone skin.

INGREDIENTS

1 banana
1 tablespoon honey
¼ orange or lemon

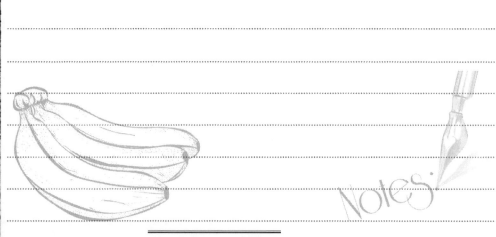

1 Peel banana, discard
peel, and place banana
in a medium bowl.

2 Add honey and mash
banana and honey together
to a thick, pasty consistency.

3 Take the quarter slice of lemon or
orange and squeeze the juice into
the banana-honey mixture and stir.

4 Apply to skin, relax, and
let sit for 20 minutes.

5 Rinse with warm
water and pat dry.

Warm Banana & Honey

This aromatic banana-honey mask will detox and nourish your skin (and it's yummolicious).

INGREDIENTS

1 ripe banana
2 tablespoons honey

Notes:

1 Warm the honey
just until it's runny.

2 Peel the banana, discard the
peel, then mash the banana
to a wet pasty consistency.

3 Add honey and
mix with spatula.

4 Place a thick layer of the mask on your
face and neck; allow yourself to simply
relax as you leave the mask on for 30 minutes.

5 Rinse with warm
water and pat dry.

Magic Tea Acne Remedy

An effective mask for skin with acne problems.
Blackwort, also known as Comfrey, is rich in allantoin —
a substance that aids regenerative skin processes.

INGREDIENTS

1 egg yolk
1 tablespoon dried blackwort plant
1 tablespoon dried chamomile flowers
1 teaspoon dried rosemary herb
2 cups filtered water
2 tablespoons potato flour

Notes:

1 Heat water in small pot; before it boils, remove from heat; add dried blackwort plant and chamomile flowers; cover the pan and let the mixture steep for several minutes; remove cover to let the "magic tea" cool.

2 Pour the magic tea through cheesecloth or a strainer and discard the plant material.

3 In separate bowl, mix egg yolk, rosemary and flour together; add small amounts of the magic tea until mixture becomes a smooth paste. Gently spread the mask evenly across your face and neck, remembering to avoid the eye area.

4 Relax and let sit for 25 minutes; rinse with the remaining magic tea and pat dry.

Sweet Carrots & Tea Tree Oil

Tea Tree oil is an anti-bacterial and anti-fungal essential oil that is great for battling acne. Green tea acts as an antioxidant, and honey helps with skin inflammation.

INGREDIENTS

2 medium carrots
1 slice pineapple
2 tablespoons honey
1 teaspoon green tea
3 drops tea tree oil

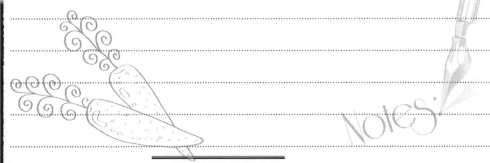

1 Brew a strong cup of green tea, (let the tea steep for at least 15 minutes), and set aside to cool.

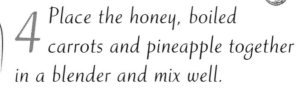

2 Boil carrots in water until soft.

3 Heat honey until it becomes a bit runny.

4 Place the honey, boiled carrots and pineapple together in a blender and mix well.

5 Add cool tea, then tea tree oil, and mix well.

6 Apply the mixture evenly to face and neck, relax, and let it sit for 20-30 minutes.

7 Rinse with warm water and pat dry.

Green Healing Blend

A healing blend of green tea and aloe vera gel.
Use only fresh, pure aloe (take it directly from the plant if
possible, as aloe doesn't keep long on the shelf).

INGREDIENTS

1 tablespoon strong green tea
4 tablespoons pure aloe vera gel
1 drop sweet orange essential oil

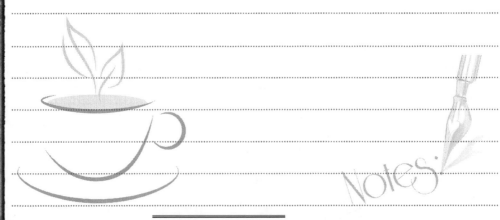

Notes:

1 Brew a strong cup of green tea (let the tea steep for at least 15 minutes), and set aside to cool.

 2 In a small bowl, mix pure aloe vera gel with about a tablespoon of green tea.

3 Add a drop of sweet orange essential oil. (If the mask is too runny add more aloe vera gel.)

 4 Smooth over face and neck avoiding the eye area; relax and leave in place for 15 minutes.

5 Rinse with warm water and pat dry.

Deep Cleaning Meow Mask

Originally, this recipe called for spreading kitty litter all over your face (only the 100% natural clay, unscented, non-clumping type, of course). Remember, the stuff is simply bentonite clay, the very same ingredient fancy-schmancy spas use to make their high-end muds and specialty clays for face and body treatments. But SOME people might not want to use kitty litter in their mask (*go figure!*), so the recipe now calls simply for a cleansing cosmetic clay powder of your choice. See the section "Clays & Kitty Litter" earlier in the book for more information.

INGREDIENTS

2 tablespoons cosmetic clay of choice
2 tablespoons warm water
¼ lemon

Notes:

1 In a small bowl squeeze lemon juice over clay.

2 Add water and mix into clay to create a spreadable mud/paste.

3 Apply thick layer of mud/paste evenly across the face and neck. Leave mask on for 10-15 minutes, but do not allow the mask to dry. Spritz with water as need to prevent drying.

4 Rinse with warm water and pat dry.

Apples, Oatmeal, Cucumber & Milk

This is fresh and lovely—great for clearing blackheads and dealing with breakouts.

INGREDIENTS

½ cup oatmeal
½ apple
¼ cucumber
2 tablespoons milk

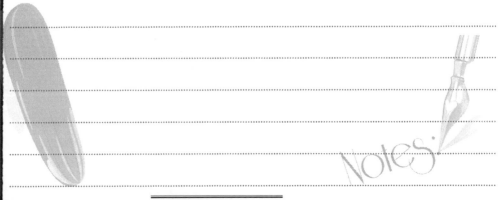

Notes:

1 Slice apple and cucumber into small pieces and mash them together in a large bowl (you may cook the apple first or mash it up raw).

2 Add oatmeal and milk; mix well until a paste forms.

3 Spread the mixture over your face and neck; relax and leave on for 20 minutes.

4 Rinse with tepid water and pat dry.

Honey, Strawberries & Cream

You may want to make a few extra batches of this one — it's so yummy, some of it is bound to wind up in your mouth. Just warning you...

INGREDIENTS

½ cup strawberries
1 teaspoon sour cream
1 teaspoon honey

Homemade Facial Masks

1 Heat the honey until it's a bit runny.

2 In a medium bowl, mash strawberries with the back of a large spoon.

3 Add honey and sour cream and mix well.

4 Use a facial brush to spread the mask on your face and neck; relax and leave it for about 20 minutes.

5 Rinse with plenty of tepid water and pat dry.

Lavender & Lemon

Green clay has extraordinary antiseptic and healing properties. At the same time, it stimulates and increases blood circulation while removing impurities. (See the section on "Clays & Kitty Litter" earlier in this book for more information about the different types of cosmetic clays). Neem oil and powder is anti-bacterial, anti-fungal and anti-viral. Try your local health food store if you don't have these ingredients in your home already.

INGREDIENTS

2 drops lavender essential oil
2 drops lemon essential oil
2 tablespoons neem powder
2 tablespoons green clay

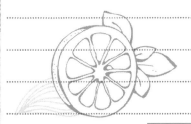

Notes:

1 In a medium size bowl, mix clay and neem powder together.

2 Add lavender and lemon essential oils and combine all ingredients until a thick paste is formed (if mixture is still too dry, add a bit of warm water until you make a spreadable mud/paste).

3 After cleansing your face, and while it is still damp, apply a thick, even layer of the clay mixture.

4 Relax and leave mask on for 10-15 minutes, but do not allow the mask to dry. Spritz with water as need to prevent drying.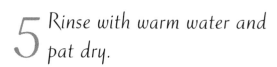

5 Rinse with warm water and pat dry.

Green Clay with Lemongrass

Homemade face masks made with clay are deep cleaning and help to unclog pores by drawing out excess oil, dirt and grime. Lemongrass and tea tree oil provide additional cleansing action, reducing bacteria that contribute to acne breakouts.

INGREDIENTS

2 teaspoons green clay
3 teaspoons plain, full-fat yogurt
2 drops lemongrass essential oil
1 drop tea tree oil

Notes

1 In a small bowl, combine clay, lemongrass essential oil, tea tree oil and yogurt.

2 Mix ingredients together to create a spreadable paste.

3 Splash some warm water on your face, then smooth the mixture on your face and neck, avoiding your eyes and mouth.

4 Relax and leave mask on for 10-15 minutes, but do not allow the mask to dry. Spritz with water as need to prevent drying.

5 Rinse with warm water and pat dry.

Citrus Moon

This is a facial peel that will help clean your pores and fight acne. You can find pure glycerin at most drug stores.

INGREDIENTS

¼ lime or lemon
¼ cup whole milk
1 teaspoon glycerin

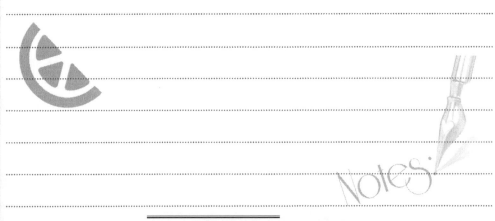

Notes:

1 To a small sauce pan, add milk and gently heat (just to warm, do not boil).

2 Squeeze the lemon or lime juice into the milk; add glycerin and stir; remove from heat and let sit.

3 When cool, apply the mixture to your face with a facial brush.

4 Leave the mask until it dries, about 20 minutes, then peel it off your skin.

5 Rinse with warm water and pat dry.

Green Magic

Cleans out pores and helps clear problem skin.

INGREDIENTS

¼ ripe papaya
1 ½ teaspoon pure aloe vera gel
4 teaspoons green clay

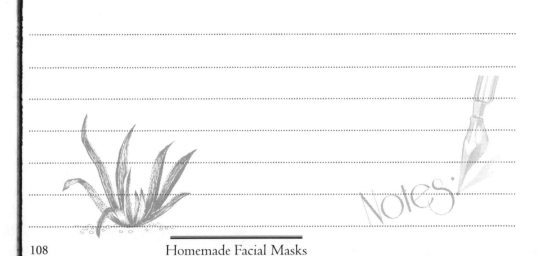

Notes:

Homemade Facial Masks

1 Remove skin and seeds from papaya and mix in a blender or food processor until smooth.

2 Move papaya to medium bowl; add pure aloe vera gel (straight from the plant is best) and green clay; mix well.

3 Smooth mixture onto damp face and neck, avoiding your eyes and mouth.

4 Leave mask on for 10-15 minutes, but do not allow the mask to dry. Spritz with water as needed to prevent drying.

5 Rinse with warm water and pat dry.

Tomato Zinger

A quick, easy mask that exfoliates, soothes and stimulates the skin's blood circulation.

INGREDIENTS

2 tablespoons tomato juice
1 teaspoon yeast
1 teaspoon plain, full-fat yogurt
½ teaspoon fresh lemon juice

Notes:

1 In a medium bowl, mix tomato juice, yeast, yogurt and lemon juice together until it becomes a paste.

2 Spread the mixture on the face and neck, and remember to avoid the skin around your eyes.

3 Leave the mask on for about 25 minutes.

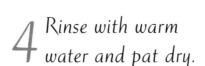

4 Rinse with warm water and pat dry.

Avocado & Almond

A wonderful, nourishing 10 minute avocado mask.

INGREDIENTS

½ ripe avocado
1 teaspoon almond oil

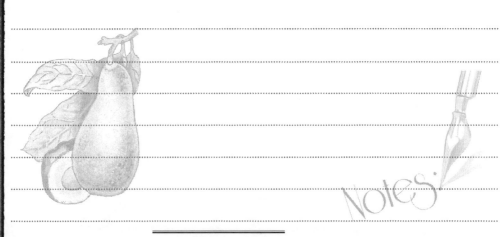

Notes:

1 Cut avocado, scoop out the meat from one half (the one without the seed) and whip the avocado with a blender or hand mixer.

2 Add almond oil to avocado mash and mix together with spatula.

3 Spread evenly over face and neck, remembering to avoid the eye area. Leave on for 10 minutes as you relax.

4 Rinse with warm water and pat dry.

Avocado & Banana

Rich and luxurious — *your skin will drink this in
and thank you for days.*

INGREDIENTS

½ ripe avocado
1 ripe banana
4 tablespoons sour cream
2 teaspoons wheat germ oil

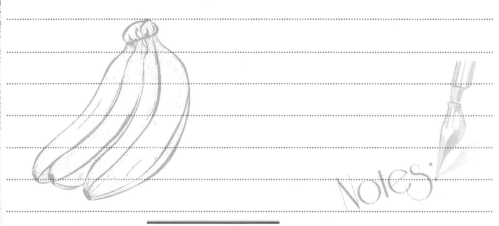

Notes:

1 Peel banana and avocado; discard banana peel and scoop avocado meat from the avocado half without the seed; place banana and avocado in blender.

2 Add sour cream and wheat germ oil and blend well.

3 Spread evenly over face and neck; leave on for 20 minutes; relax and enjoy.

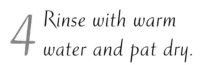

4 Rinse with warm water and pat dry.

Avocado & Olive Oil Supreme

A simple and supremely nourishing mask for dry skin.

INGREDIENTS

½ ripe avocado
1 tablespoon olive oil

Notes:

1 Peel avocado, scoop the meat from one half (the one without the seed); use a blender, food processor or hand mixer to whip avocado.

2 Add olive oil and blend for a few more seconds.

 3 Spread evenly over face and neck; relax and leave for 30 minutes.

4 Rinse with warm water and pat dry.

Avocado Sunrise

To cleanse and moisturize in the most delightful way.

INGREDIENTS

½ ripe avocado
½ cup buttermilk
1 egg yolk

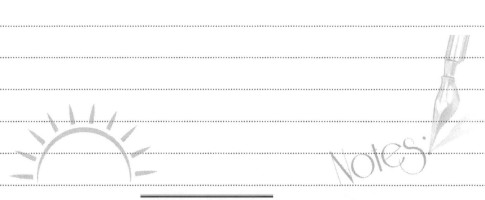

1 Peel ripe avocado, scoop out the meat of one half (the one without the seed); with a blender or hand mixer, smash and then whip avocado.

2 Add buttermilk and egg yolk to mixture and blend a bit more.

3 Spread ½ of the mixture evenly over face and neck, avoiding the eye area, and leave for 5 minutes.

4 Spread remaining mixture on face and neck and leave for another 15 minutes.

5 Rinse with warm water and pat dry.

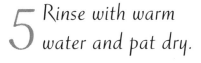

Banana & Vitamin E

A simple, moisturizing mask featuring banana and vitamin E.

INGREDIENTS

1 ripe banana
4 gel capsules vitamin E

Notes:

1 Peel banana and discard the peel; in a medium bowl, mash the banana with the back of a large spoon.

2 Prick or cut off a piece of the vitamin E gel caps and squeeze contents into the banana mash; mix well.

3 Avoiding the eye area, apply evenly to face and neck and leave on for 5-10 minutes.

4 Rinse with warm water and pat dry.

Creamy Brown Sugar

Brown sugar gently exfoliates skin (remember, <u>gentle</u> is key—no scrubbing) and milk is a delicate moisturizer. This mask feels and smells divine.

INGREDIENTS

¼ cup brown sugar
2 tablespoons whole milk

Notes:

1 In a medium bowl, mix brown sugar and milk together well.

2 Drape a towel around your neck (it's a fluid mixture and tends to run).

3 Using your fingers, scoop the mixture into one hand and use the other to gently spread across face and neck area, avoiding your eyes; massage into skin with very gentle circular motion for about one minute; let mixture sit for about 20 minutes.

4 Rinse with warm water and pat dry.

Chocolate Dream

This moisturizing mask smells so good you'll be tempted to inhale it while you're wearing it.

INGREDIENTS

1 tablespoon cocoa powder
1 tablespoon heavy cream
1 teaspoon cottage cheese
4 teaspoons honey, warm
1 teaspoon oatmeal

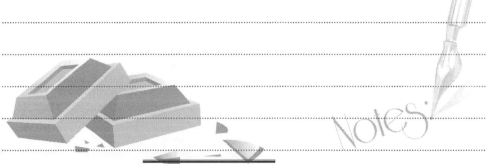

Notes:

1 Warm honey to a runny consistency.

2 Add cocoa powder, cream, cottage cheese, honey and dry oatmeal to a blender or food processor and blend.

3 Apply with facial brush to freshly cleaned face; relax, enjoy, sneak a taste and leave on for 30 minutes.

4 Rinse with warm water and pat dry.

Chocolate Fantasy

Here is a delicious chocolate mask you'll want to share.

INGREDIENTS

1 tablespoon cocoa powder
1 tablespoon honey
2 teaspoons sour cream
1 tablespoon oatmeal

1 Place cocoa powder, honey, sour cream and dry oatmeal in a blender or food processor and blend to a rich, smooth consistency.

2 Apply evenly to face and neck; relax, and allow mask to sit for 15 minutes.

3 Rinse with warm water and pat dry.

Moisturizing Milk & Honey

This sticky sweet mask moisturizes and nourishes dry skin.

INGREDIENTS

1 teaspoon powdered milk
1 tablespoon honey
1 teaspoon aloe vera gel
2 drops lavender essential oil
1 tablespoon almond flour

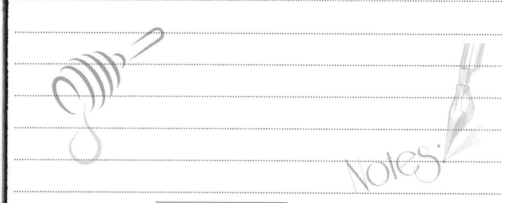

1 In a medium bowl, combine powdered milk, honey and fresh aloe vera gel (straight from the aloe plant is best).

2 Add almond flour (or substitute pulverized almonds) and lavender oil; mix well.

3 Cleanse face and, while still damp, spread mask evenly across face and neck area; relax and let sit for 25 minutes.

4 Rinse with warm water and pat dry.

Cranberry Facial Mask

Exfoliate and add moisture with this easy, delicious mask that's perfect to share. Make it a special treat during the holidays if you have cranberries in the kitchen.

INGREDIENTS

15 whole, fresh cranberries
1 tablespoon dry oatmeal
2 tablespoons whipping cream
1 tablespoon almond flour

Notes:

1 Place cranberries in a blender or food processor and blend well.

2 Add oatmeal, whipping cream and almond flour; mix well until smooth.

3 Apply very gently to face and neck in a light circular motion, careful to avoid the eye area.

4 Relax and let sit for 20 minutes; rinse with warm water and pat dry.

Golden Dew

This combination of egg, olive oil and honey will leave your skin soft and dewy.

INGREDIENTS

1 egg yolk
1 tablespoon honey
1 teaspoon olive oil

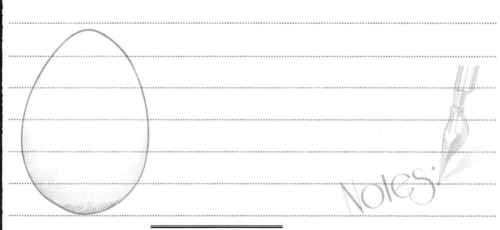

Notes:

1 Warm the honey until
it is a bit runny.

 2 In a small bowl,
combine egg yolk, honey
and olive oil; mix well.

3 Apply evenly to skin
with facial brush.

 4 Leave on for 25
minutes; rinse with
warm water and pat dry.

Morning Glory

Your skin will glow after using this rich, luxurious facial mask.

INGREDIENTS

1 egg
½ teaspoon olive oil
1 tablespoon flour
¼ teaspoon table sugar
1 tablespoon whole milk

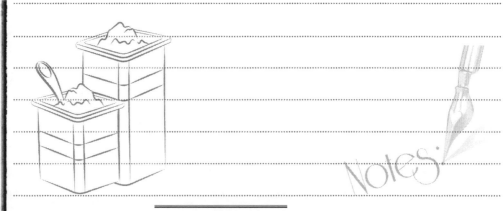

Notes:

1 In a medium bowl mix together
olive oil, flour and milk.

2 Add egg to mixture,
and stir; add sugar last.

3 Apply to your face and neck
with fingers in gentle circular
motion for about 2 minutes; let
sit for 20 minutes as you relax.

4 Rinse with warm water, then
with cool water and pat dry.

Soothing Banana

*A banana facial mask that gently exfoliates as it
nourishes without over-drying.*

INGREDIENTS

1 banana
1 tablespoon wheat germ
¼ teaspoon jojoba oil

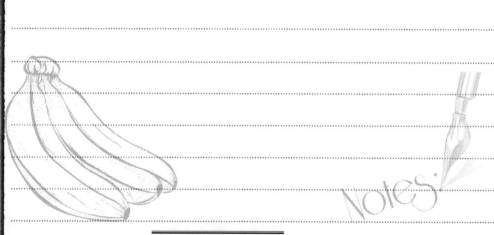

Notes:

1 Peel banana and discard the peel; in a small bowl mash the banana to a paste-like consistency with the back of a large spoon.

2 Stir in jojoba oil.

3 Add wheat germ and mix well.

4 With fingers, spread evenly across face and neck; gently rub mixture in a circular motion for about 1 minute; relax and let sit for 15 minutes.

5 Rinse with warm water and pat dry.

Hydrating Age Buster

This facial mask recipe is super-nourishing for skin that is particularly dry or damaged. It's packed with inexpensive ingredients that offer healing, age-defying benefits. Use this recipe regularly for a few months and notice the difference in the tone, clarity and smoothness of your skin.

INGREDIENTS

2 tablespoons white (also called kaolin) clay

1 egg yolk

1 teaspoon sour cream

½ teaspoon honey

½ teaspoon apple cider vinegar

1 teaspoon jojoba oil

2 drops sandalwood essential oil

2 drops rosewood essential oil

Notes:

1 In a small bowl, whisk together egg yolk, sour cream, honey, apple cider vinegar, jojoba oil, sandalwood oil and rosewood oil.

2 Slowly add the clay, a little at a time, stirring thoroughly to create a spreadable paste. If the mixture seems too thick, add a little more sour cream or a splash of milk (do not increase the amount of oil).

3 Cleanse face; while still damp, smooth mask over your face and neck, avoiding your eyes and mouth.

4 Relax and leave mask on for 10-15 minutes, but do not allow the mask to dry. Spritz with water as needed to prevent drying.

5 Rinse with warm water and pat dry.

Beer & Yogurt

The yeast in beer is a lovely skin cleanser;
the yogurt and egg add moisture.

INGREDIENTS

1 tablespoon beer
1 egg yolk
2 teaspoons plain, full-fat yogurt
1 teaspoon olive oil
1 teaspoon lemon extract
1 teaspoon almond extract

Notes:

1 In a medium bowl, combine beer, egg yolk, yogurt, olive oil, lemon extract, and almond extract.

2 Mix for thirty seconds on low speed if using a powered hand mixer (or mix by hand until well blended).

3 Cleanse your face; while it's still damp, apply to face and neck with facial brush—remembering to avoid eye area—and let sit for 20 minutes.

4 Rinse with warm water and pat dry.

Rejuvenating Oatmeal

Oatmeal face masks are soothing, encourage skin rejuvenation and are a great source of moisture for the skin. This recipe is enough for two masks, so go ahead—invite a friend to share the magic!

INGREDIENTS

1 cup dry oatmeal
1 teaspoon honey
2 tablespoons plain, full-fat yogurt
1 teaspoon buttermilk
1 ripe tomato
¼ small lemon (or lime)

1 Place dry oatmeal in blender or food processor and blend to a slightly powdered consistency.

2 Add buttermilk, yogurt, honey and tomato, and squeeze the juice from the lemon (or lime) into mixture; mix until you have a paste-like consistency.

3 Smooth mask evenly across face and neck, careful to avoid the eye area; leave it on for 15 minutes and remember your favorite part of the day.

4 Rinse with warm water and pat dry.

Rosewood Miracle Mask

Rosewood is a tropical, evergreen tree and its essential oil has been used to treat acne, candida, depression, eczema, dry skin and more. It is antibacterial, antifungal, anti-infectious, antiparasitic and antiviral. It's an amazing skin rejuvenator and is said to create skin elasticity, regenerate tissue and slow the aging process.

INGREDIENTS

2 tablespoons table sugar
2 tablespoons plain, full-fat yogurt
2 drops rosewood essential oil

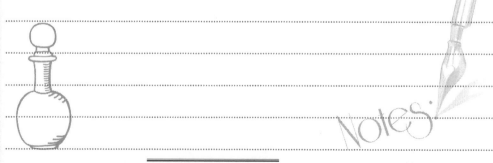

Notes:

1 In a small bowl, add sugar to plain, full-fat yogurt and mix together.

2 Add rosewood oil.

3 Cleanse face; while still damp, massage mixture into skin with very gentle circular motion for 2-3 minutes.

4 Relax and let sit for 10 minutes; rinse with warm water and pat dry.

Yogurt Walnut No-Scrub

This is a simple, delightful "scrub," but as always, be very careful and gentle with this one. Remember the cardinal rule: Do no harm (and scrubbing too much or too aggressively=harm). Be gentle, and the nuts will exfoliate old dry skin while the yogurt sooths your skin. Be sure the walnuts are finely ground and, as with any of the exfoliating scrubs, do not overuse the mask and be very gentle with it.

INGREDIENTS

¼ cup plain, full-fat yogurt
¼ cup walnuts

1 Grind or pulverize walnuts until extremely fine (they will look almost flour-like).

2 In a small bowl, combine yogurt and walnuts and mix well.

3 Use your fingers to _gently_ massage mixture into your skin for about 3 minutes.

4 Rinse with warm water and pat dry.

Apricot & Yogurt

Add a youthful glow to your skin with apricots and yogurt.

INGREDIENTS

1 medium apricot; pitted and peeled
2 tablespoons plain, full-fat yogurt

1 Peel apricot and remove pit.

2 Place yogurt and apricot in a blender or food processor; blend well.

3 Apply evenly to face and neck with fingers or a facial brush; leave mask on for 20 minutes and relax.

4 Rinse with warm water and pat dry.

Banana Avocado Combo

A simple and effective recipe to nourish and protect combination skin.

INGREDIENTS

½ banana
½ avocado
2 tablespoons plain, full-fat yogurt
1 teaspoon olive oil

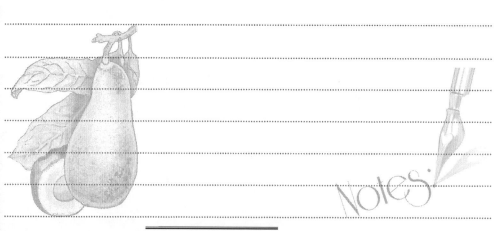

Notes:

1 Peel banana and avocado; discard banana peel and scoop avocado meat from one half without the seed; place banana and avocado in blender.

2 Add yogurt and olive oil; puree all ingredients until smooth.

3 Apply evenly to freshly cleaned face; relax and let sit for 15 minutes.

4 Rinse with warm water and pat dry.

Blueberry Cream Combo

This delicious blueberry mask tones and moisturizes skin. It's great for normal or combination skin and smells divine.

INGREDIENTS

15-20 fresh blueberries
½ cup plain, full-fat yogurt

1 Place blueberries in hot steamer for 2-3 minutes; remove and let sit.

2 When blueberries are cool to touch, place them in blender or food processor.

3 Add yogurt to blender and whip ingredients until fluffy.

4 Apply mask with fingers to face and neck in a light, circular motion, remembering to avoid the eye area.

5 Relax, breathe in the delicious aroma, and leave on for 30 minutes; rinse with warm water and pat dry.

Honey Almond Elastin Booster

A power combination to nourish and promote healthy, glowing skin.

INGREDIENTS

1 tablespoon honey, warm
2 tablespoons almonds
1 teaspoon powdered clay
4 tablespoons oatmeal

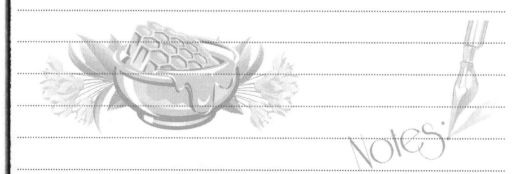

Homemade Facial Masks

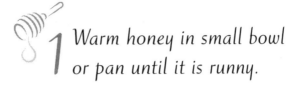

1 Warm honey in small bowl or pan until it is runny.

2 Place almonds and dry oatmeal in a blender or food processor and pulse until they are very finely crushed (to a flour-like consistency).

3 Add clay and warm honey; blend well. If the mixture seems too thick, add a splash of warm water (but do not add too much water; for this mask, thicker is better).

4 Apply evenly to face and neck, avoiding the eye area; relax and leave on for 15 minutes; rinse with warm water and a wet wash cloth; pat dry.

Sweet Orange Wonder

A delicious mask that is easy and fun. It tightens and softens skin as it cleans your pores.

INGREDIENTS

1 tablespoon honey, warm
¼ orange

Notes:

1 Warm the honey in a small bowl until it is a bit runny.

2 Squeeze the juice from the orange slice into the honey and mix well.

 3 Using a facial brush, apply evenly to your face and neck, avoiding the eye area.

4 Leave on for 20 minutes; relax, breathe and enjoy.

5 Rinse with warm water and pat dry.

Sweet Rosewater

This delicate mask calls for rosewater, yogurt and honey to balance the oily and dry areas of your skin.

INGREDIENTS

2 tablespoons rosewater
1 tablespoon plain, full-fat yogurt
1 tablespoon honey, warm

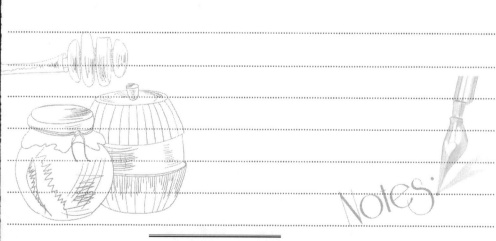

1 Warm honey until it becomes a bit runny.

2 In a medium bowl combine rosewater, yogurt and honey; mix well.

3 Apply evenly to skin with facial brush.

4 Relax, and let sit for 15 minutes; rinse with warm water and pat dry.

Milk & Sugar Cookie

Use this fun and delicious facial "scrub" for glowing skin, but **DON'T SCRUB**. Any time you exfoliate, be very careful not to rub too hard or scrub too vigorously—that can easily damage your skin. Gentle, occasional exfoliation is the aim. Now enjoy!

INGREDIENTS

½ cup fine grain table sugar
½ cup whole milk
1 tablespoon sweet almond oil
1 teaspoon vanilla extract

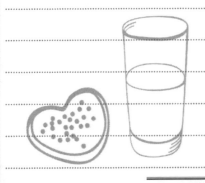

1 In a medium bowl combine sugar, milk, almond oil and vanilla extract; mix well.

2 Drape a towel around your neck.

3 Use your fingers to spread the grainy liquid in gentle, circular motions across the face and neck.

4 Rinse with warm water and pat dry.

Sugar and Spice No-Scrub

This facial mask doubles as a "scrub," but any time you exfoliate your skin, be extremely careful not to rub too hard or scrub too vigorously—that can damage your skin, which violates the first cardinal rule of skin care. That's why I like to call this one a "no-scrub scrub." Still, gentle, occasional exfoliation is fabulous for your skin. And this recipe is a fabulous way to do that.

INGREDIENTS

½ cup granulated sugar
½ cup dark brown sugar
½ cup sweet almond oil
2 teaspoons pure vanilla extract
1 tablespoon dry oatmeal
½ teaspoon cinnamon

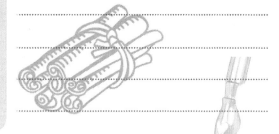

1 Place dry oatmeal in blender or food processor and blend until it is a fine powder.

2 Transfer oatmeal to a large bowl and add sugar, brown sugar, sweet almond oil, vanilla extract and cinnamon; stir ingredients until mixed well.

3 Using your fingers, apply mixture evenly to face with very gentle circular motion for about 2 minutes. Relax and let sit for 20 minutes.

4 Rinse with warm water and pat dry.

Gentle Soothing Relief

INGREDIENTS

½ tablespoon clay
½ tablespoon rolled oats
½ teaspoon olive oil
½ teaspoon fresh aloe vera gel
   (straight from the plant is best)
½ teaspoon honey
½ teaspoon whole milk
 1 drop chamomile essential oil
 2 drops rosewood essential oil
 1 drop lavender essential oil

This homemade face mask is deep cleaning. It's also designed to soothe red, irritated skin and to help reduce itchy, scaly patches caused by eczema or psoriasis.

Notes:

1 Grind the oats to a very fine powder in a blender or food processor.

2 Heat honey so that it is a bit runny.

3 In a small bowl, mix together the olive oil, fresh aloe vera, milk and honey until completely combined.

4 Slowly add clay and oat powder a little at a time, stirring thoroughly to create a spreadable paste. (If the mixture seems too thick, add a splash more milk. Do not increase the oil).

5 Stir in the chamomile, rosewood and lavender essential oils.

6 Cleanse your face and then, while it's still damp, smooth the mask onto your face and neck, avoiding your eyes and mouth.

7 Relax and leave mask in place for 25 minutes; rinse with warm water and a wet washcloth; pat dry.

Butter, Yogurt & Oatmeal

Plain old butter is a great source of vitamin A. Vitamin A helps to rejuvenate skin, improve its texture and stimulate blood supplies to collagen fibers deep within the skin.

INGREDIENTS

1 tablespoon butter
1 tablespoon plain, full-fat yogurt
½ tablespoon dry oatmeal

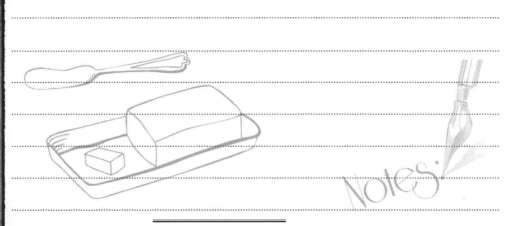

1 Melt butter and set aside to cool.

2 Grind or crush oatmeal to a powder (you can use a coffee grinder, food processor or a mortar and pestle).

3 In a medium bowl, combine butter, oatmeal and yogurt; mix together until fairly smooth.

 4 Apply evenly to face and neck with fingers or using a facial brush; relax and leave in place for 15 minutes.

5 Rinse with warm water and pat dry.

Green Honey Banana

This mask tightens and refreshes with banana,
honey, mint, ginger and more.

INGREDIENTS

1 ripe banana
3 tablespoons honey, warm
2 egg whites
4 cups fresh spinach
1 cup fresh mint
1 one-inch piece of ginger

Notes:

1 Rinse spinach and mint; peel ginger and banana and discard the peels.

2 Place spinach, mint and ginger in blender or food processor and pulse until finely chopped.

3 Add banana and honey; continue to blend all ingredients until liquid.

4 Add egg whites and continue blending.

5 Apply to face and neck, avoiding the eye area; relax and leave in place for 20 minutes.

6 Rinse with warm water and pat dry.

Honey & Ricotta Cheese

Honey and ricotta cheese make a wonderful combination for a facial mask. The honey plus the fat in the cheese nourishes your skin.

INGREDIENTS

¼ cup ricotta cheese
2 tablespoons honey

Notes:

1 Warm honey until it becomes a bit runny.

2 In a small bowl, combine honey and ricotta cheese.

3 Apply mixture evenly to your face and neck with a facial brush.

4 Relax, and leave on for 20 minutes; rinse with warm water and pat dry.

Simply Divine

This effective, easy to make homemade facial mask recipe is designed to balance, hydrate and cleanse normal skin types.

INGREDIENTS

1 tablespoon cosmetic clay
1 teaspoon plain, full-fat yogurt
½ teaspoon honey
¼ teaspoon jojoba oil
1 drop lavender essential oil
1 drop rosewood essential oil

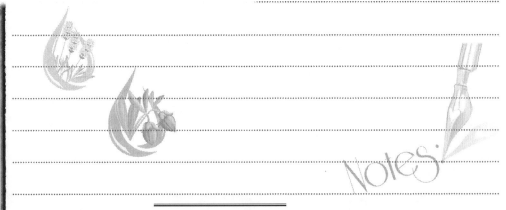

Notes:

1 Warm honey until it is a bit runny.

2 In a small bowl whisk together yogurt, honey, jojoba oil, lavender essential oil and rosewood essential oil.

3 Slowly add the clay, a little at a time, stirring thoroughly to create a spreadable paste. (If the mixture seems too thick, add a little more yogurt or a splash of milk).

4 Cleanse your face and, while still damp, smooth the mask over your face and neck, avoiding your eyes and mouth.

5 Relax, and leave it on 30 minutes; rinse with warm water and a wet washcloth; pat dry.

Simply Delicious

This yummy recipe is designed to even skin tone and hydrate normal skin types.

INGREDIENTS

1 teaspoon plain, full-fat yogurt
½ teaspoon honey, warm
¼ teaspoon olive oil
2 drops sweet orange essential oil

1 Warm honey until it's a bit runny.

2 In a small bowl, combine yogurt, honey and olive oil; mix well.

3 Add sweet orange essential oil and stir gently.

4 With a facial brush, smooth mixture over your face and neck, avoiding the eye area.

5 Relax and let sit 25 minutes; rinse with warm water and pat dry.

Anti-Aging Facial Mask

This mask will help tighten your skin as it refreshes you with aroma-therapy.

INGREDIENTS

1 tablespoon cosmetic clay
1 tablespoon dry oatmeal
1 teaspoon honey
1 teaspoon almond oil
1 drop lavender essential oil
2 drops rosewood essential oil

Notes:

1 Grind dry oatmeal to a fine powder with a coffee grinder or food processor.

2 Warm honey to a runny consistency.

3 In a small bowl, stir together oatmeal, honey, almond oil, lavender essential oil and rosewood essential oil until well blended.

4 Slowly add the clay, a little at a time, stirring thoroughly to create a spreadable paste. (If the mixture seems too thick, add a little water or a splash of milk).

5 Apply evenly to face and neck while avoiding the eyes and mouth. Leave on for 20 minutes; rinse with warm water and gentle wipe any remaining mask away with a wet washcloth; pat dry.

Honey Apple

Try this delightful apple and honey combination
to open, cleanse and refine your pores.

INGREDIENTS

1 medium apple
2 tablespoons honey

Notes:

1 Peel, core and chop apple into pieces. (If apple is too hard or crisp, you may boil it for a minute or so to make it softer).

2 Warm honey until it is a bit runny.

3 Place apple and honey in blender and puree.

4 Apply to your face and neck using fingers or a facial brush. (Yes, you can have a bite too — but save enough for your facial).

5 Relax and leave mask on for 20 minutes; rinse with warm water and pat dry.

Sour Apple

This sassy combo soothes and revitalizes tired skin.

INGREDIENTS

1 medium apple
2 tablespoons sour cream

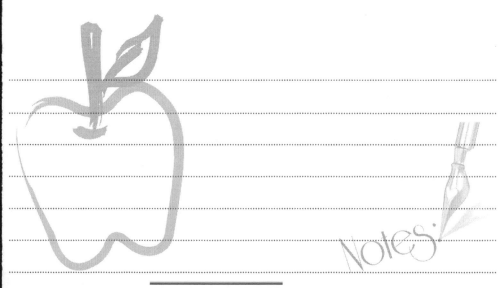

1 Peel, core and chop apple into pieces.
  (If apple is too hard or crisp, you may
boil it for a minute or so to soften it up.)

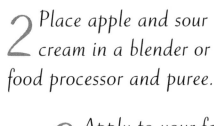

2 Place apple and sour
  cream in a blender or
food processor and puree.

3 Apply to your face and
  neck; relax and leave
mask on for 15 minutes.

4 Rinse with warm
  water and pat dry.

Creamy Apricot

Refresh and revitalize your skin with this yummy,
moisture-packed facial mask.

INGREDIENTS

½ cup dried apricots
½ cup warm water
1 tablespoon dry milk powder
1 tablespoon honey

1 Warm honey until it 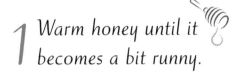 becomes a bit runny.

2 Place apricots, dry milk powder, honey and water in blender or food processor and blend until smooth.

3 Apply to your face and neck avoiding the eye area.

 4 Relax and leave mask on for 25 minutes.

5 Rinse with warm water and pat dry.

Simply Avocado

Simple. Easy. And leaves your skin surprisingly nourished and soft to the touch.

INGREDIENTS

½ avocado

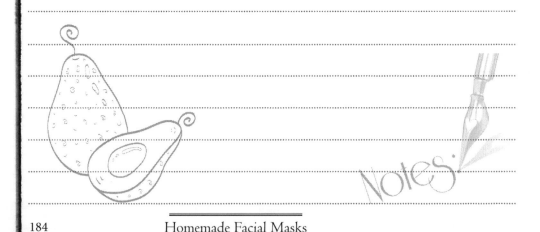

1 Peel ripe avocado, scoop out the meat of one half (the one without the seed) and mash the avocado with a mortar and pestle or spoon.

2 Apply evenly to your face and neck, avoiding the eye area.

3 Relax and leave on for 20 minutes.

4 Rinse with warm water and pat dry.

Banana Oatmeal

Bananas have fruit acids that help to gently slough away dead skin. Try this invigorating facial mask to give your complexion an unmistakable glow.

INGREDIENTS

1 ripe banana
½ cup dry oatmeal

Notes:

1 Peel banana, discard peel; place banana in medium bowl.

2 Add oatmeal and mash into the soft peeled banana a little at a time with your fingers (or you can use the back of a large spoon). Continue until all of the oatmeal is moistened.

3 Apply evenly to your face and neck; relax, count 7 of your favorite blessings, and leave on for 30 minutes.

4 Rinse with warm water and pat dry.

Creamy Cucumber

This is a simple, soothing, revitalizing mask for every day.

INGREDIENTS

½ cucumber
1 tablespoon plain, full-fat yogurt

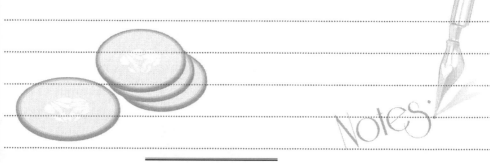

1 Peel and slice cucumber.

2 Place cucumber and yogurt in blender or food processor and puree.

3 Apply evenly to your face and neck, avoiding the area around the eyes; relax and leave on for 30 minutes or longer.

4 Rinse with warm water and pat dry.

All Skin Types

Cucumber & Mint Refresher

Enjoy the cool, minty feeling of this classic cucumber facial with a twist.

INGREDIENTS

½ cucumber
1 tablespoon plain, full-fat yogurt
1 tablespoon non-fat dry milk
5 fresh mint leaves

Notes:

1 Peel and slice cucumber.

2 Place cucumber, yogurt, dry milk and mint leaves in blender or food processor and blend until smooth.

3 Apply evenly to your face and neck, avoiding the eyes; relax, breathe deeply, and think about all that you are grateful for as you let the mask sit for about 15 minutes.

4 Rinse with warm water and pat dry.

Yellow Cream

Refresh your outlook with this simple,
creamy, nourishing mask.

INGREDIENTS

1 egg
1 teaspoon honey, warm
1 teaspoon heavy cream

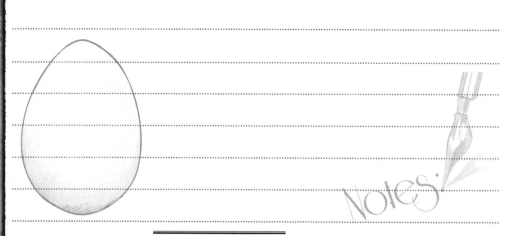

Homemade Facial Masks

1 In a small bowl combine egg, honey and heavy cream and blend well (if mixture is too runny, add another teaspoon of honey to thicken).

2 Apply evenly to your face and neck with facial brush, avoiding the area around your eyes; relax and leave on for 15 minutes.

3 Rinse with warm water and pat dry.

Refreshingly Delicious

Here's a yummy, refreshing mask that's fun to share.
Your friends will love it, and your skin will too.

INGREDIENTS

¼ apple
½ peach
½ tomato
¼ cup whole milk

Notes:

Homemade Facial Masks

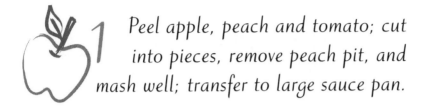

1 Peel apple, peach and tomato; cut into pieces, remove peach pit, and mash well; transfer to large sauce pan.

2 Add milk and cook over moderate heat, stirring until the mixture takes on a cream-like consistency; then let mixture sit.

3 When cool, apply evenly to your face and neck, avoiding the eyes; leave on for 20 minutes as you relax and enjoy.

4 Rinse with warm water and pat dry.

Starry Eyes

For beautiful, healthy skin try this mask that especially combats puffiness and rejuvenates delicate skin around the eyes.

INGREDIENTS

1 tablespoon almond oil
1 tablespoon olive oil
1 tablespoon wheat germ oil
3 drops rosewood essential oil
3 gel capsules vitamin E

Notes:

1 In a small bowl, combine almond oil, olive oil, wheat germ oil and rosewood essential oil and mix well.

2 Prick or cut end from vitamin E gel caps, squeeze contents into bowl, and continue to mix.

3 With a small facial brush, carefully apply mixture to skin under and around eyes (do not get inside eyes); leave for 30 minutes and relax.

4 Gently rinse with tepid water, very gently wiping away any remaining mask with warm, wet washcloth.

Smooth Sensation

This aromatic, creamy facial mask leaves your skin looking and feeling sensationally smooth.

INGREDIENTS

½ ripe banana
½ ripe avocado
½ cucumber
1 tablespoon plain, full-fat yogurt
1 tablespoon olive oil

1 Peel banana, avocado and cucumber; scoop out the meat of one half of the avocado (the one without the seed); and place all in blender or food processor.

2 Add yogurt and olive oil and blend well.

3 Apply a thick layer to face and neck; leave on for 30 minutes and relax.

4 Rinse well with warm water and pat dry.

For All Skin Types

All Skin Types

Firming Peach Mask

For firm, radiant skin.

INGREDIENTS

1 ripe peach
1 egg white
1 teaspoon plain, full-fat yogurt

Notes:

1 Peel peach, discard peel and pit, and place in blender or food processor.

2 Add egg white, yogurt and blend well.

3 Apply to freshly cleaned face and leave on for 15 minutes as you relax and enjoy a few moments to yourself.

 4 Rinse with warm water and pat dry.

Peaches & Honey

Ready for skin like peaches and honey?
Give this delicious mask recipe a try!

INGREDIENTS

1 ripe peach
1 tablespoon honey, warm
1 tablespoon plain, full-fat yogurt

Notes:

1 Remove peach pit and skin; cut peach into several pieces.

2 In a medium bowl, add peach slices and mash together with back of large spoon. (If peach is not soft enough to mash, you can boil the peach until it's soft enough).

3 Add warm honey and yogurt; blend well.

4 Apply to the face neck; relax and leave on for 20 minutes.

5 Rinse with warm water and pat dry.

Fountain of Youth

For a dewy, youthful glow.

INGREDIENTS

2 teaspoons sour cream
½ teaspoon honey, warm
¼ teaspoon lemon juice
3 capsules vitamin E

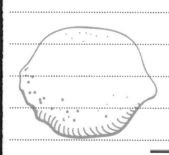

Notes

1 In a small bowl, combine sour cream, warm honey and lemon juice.

2 Prick vitamin E capsules and squeeze contents into bowl; mix well.

3 Apply to face and neck, avoiding the eye area (you may want to use a facial brush for this one); relax and leave on for 10 to 15 minutes.

4 Rinse with warm water and pat dry.

Herbal Delight

A truly refreshing mask, this recipe calls for fresh mint and dried chamomile flowers.

INGREDIENTS

1 whole egg
1 tablespoon honey
1 teaspoon dried chamomile flowers
1 teaspoon finely chopped fresh mint
1 tablespoon plain, full-fat yogurt

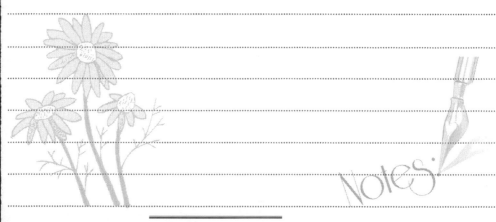

Notes:

1 Using a mortar and pestle, mash mint and chamomile flowers together (you can use the back of a spoon and a small bowl if you prefer).

2 Placed crushed herbs in small bowl; add egg, honey and plain, full-fat yogurt and mix well.

3 Apply to your face and neck; relax and let sit until dry (about 10-15 minutes).

4 Rinse with warm water and pat dry.

All Skin Types

Quicksilver Cream

This is a quick and easy mask with nice results.
It will leave your skin feeling smooth and supple.

INGREDIENTS

1 tablespoon heavy cream
1 tablespoon honey
1 teaspoon baking soda
¼ teaspoon lemon juice
3 capsules vitamin E

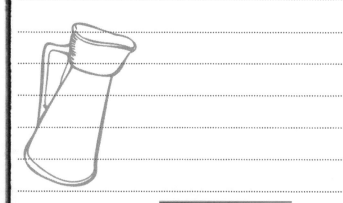

Notes:

1 In a small bowl, mix baking soda with cream until it acquires the consistency of mousse or shaving foam (an electric mixer works best for this).

2 Prick or cut the ends from the vitamin E capsules and squeeze contents into bowl.

3 Add honey and lemon juice and mix well.

4 Smooth mask over face and neck with fingers or a facial bush; relax and let sit for 20 minutes.

5 Rinse with warm water and pat dry.

Holiday Aroma

You needn't wait for the weather to turn cold. Enjoy the comfort and aroma of the holidays today as you enjoy the benefits of this facial mask.

INGREDIENTS

2 tablespoons honey, warm
1 tablespoon whole milk
1 teaspoon vanilla extract
½ teaspoon cinnamon
1 tablespoon yogurt

Vanilla

Notes:

1 In a medium bowl, add yogurt, warm honey, milk, vanilla and cinnamon; stir to mix ingredients well.

 2 Apply mask with facial brush to face and neck; relax and let sit for 20 minutes.

3 Breathe deeply, relax, and enjoy.

 4 Rinse with warm water and pat dry.

Dewdrop Mist

Moisturize your face with this delightful facial mask.

INGREDIENTS

1 tablespoon heavy cream
1 teaspoon cottage cheese
1 teaspoon honey
1 teaspoon oatmeal
¼ teaspoon lemon juice
3 capsules vitamin E

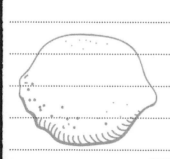

Notes

1 Grind oatmeal in coffee grinder or with mortar and pestle to a coarse flour consistency.

2 In a small bowl, add cream, cottage cheese, honey, lemon juice and oatmeal; mix.

3 Prick or cut end from 3 vitamin E capsules and squeeze contents into bowl; mix well.

4 Smooth onto face and neck with fingers or a facial brush; as always, avoid the area around your eyes; relax and let sit for 10 minutes.

5 Rinse with warm water and pat dry.

All Skin Types

Almond Omelet

A lovely mask you'll want to apply with a facial brush.

INGREDIENTS

1 egg
1 teaspoon almond oil
1 tablespoon half and half
1 tablespoon yogurt

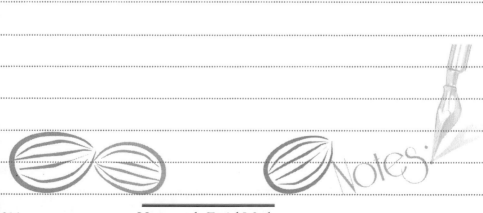

1 In a small bowl, whisk egg.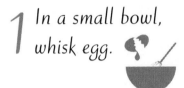

2 Add almond oil, half and half and yogurt and mix well.

3 Apply to face and neck with facial brush (mixture will be liquid!) and leave on for about 20 minutes.

4 Rinse with tepid water and pat dry.

Minty Oatmeal Mask

This is a cleansing, nourishing and refreshing mask.

INGREDIENTS

½ ripe banana
1 egg white
1 teaspoon mint tea
1 cup oatmeal
¼ teaspoon lemon juice

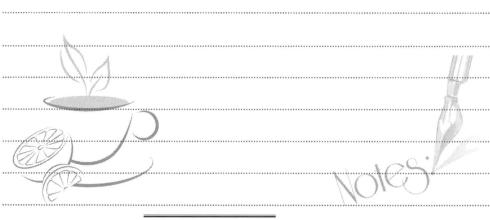

1 Make a cup of hot mint tea, then set aside to cool (drink some while you finish making your mask if you like!).

2 Peel banana and discard peel; in a medium bowl, mash banana with back of large spoon.

3 To banana mash, add egg white, lemon juice, cooled mint tea and oatmeal; mix well.

4 Apply mask to your face and neck, careful to avoid area around the eyes.

5 Relax and leave on until it dries; rinse with warm water and pat dry.

Orange Yogurt

This facial cleans pores and nourishes the skin. It feels cool and refreshing and is a perfect pick-me-up for those days you're feeling a bit sluggish.

INGREDIENTS

¼ orange
1 tablespoon plain, full-fat yogurt

Notes:

1 In small bowl, mix yogurt and juice from orange and mix well.

2 Spread mixture with hands or facial brush over face and neck, careful to avoid the eye area; leave on for about 5 minutes (no more than 10 minutes).

3 Rinse with warm water and pat dry.

Peppy Papaya

A simple and easy to make mask using papaya.

INGREDIENTS

½ papaya

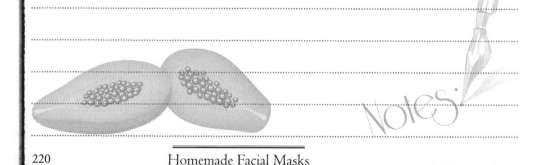

Notes

1 Peel papaya and remove seeds.

2 Chop into pieces and, using a blender or food processor, blend until papaya is the consistency of baby food.

3 Spread over face and neck with fingers or with a facial brush; let sit and relax for 15 minutes.

4 Rinse with warm water and pat dry.

Peachy Perfection

This mask smells wonderful and is perfectly refreshing on a hot summer day.

INGREDIENTS

1 soft, medium-size peach
1 tablespoon honey
1 tablespoon oatmeal
1 tablespoon yogurt

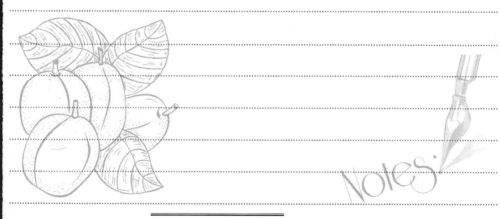

Notes:

1 Remove peach pit and slice peach into several pieces; mash the peach pieces in medium bowl with the back of a large spoon.

2 Add honey, oatmeal and yogurt to peaches and mix well.

3 Apply to face and neck; relax and let sit for 15 minutes.

4 Rinse with warm water and pat dry.

Pineapple Dreams

This yummy face mask will tighten and nourish
your skin like in your dreams.

INGREDIENTS

4 pineapple chunks
1 tablespoon heavy whipping cream
1 tablespoon honey
2 tablespoons ground oats
3 capsules vitamin E

Notes:

1 Place pineapple chunks into blender and pulse to a thick mash.

2 Add honey, cream and oats.

3 Poke a hole (or cut off the very edge) of the vitamin E caps and squeeze contents into mixture; blend until final consistency is something between a thick cream and a lumpy paste.

4 Apply to your face and neck, taking care to avoid the eye area; relax and leave on for 25 minutes.

5 Rinse with warm water and pat dry.

Pumpkin & Olive Oil

This yummy pumpkin mask helps smooth,
moisturize and nourish your skin.

INGREDIENTS

2 cups canned pumpkin
1 tablespoon olive oil
4 tablespoons honey; warmed
   a sprinkle pumpkin pie spice
1 tablespoon yogurt

Notes:

1 Mash the pumpkin and the olive oil together, if too thick add more oil.

2 Stir in warmed honey, yogurt and pumpkin pie spice.

3 Apply to your face and wait for 20 minutes.

4 Rinse with warm water.

Cucumber Fresh

Need to make your face feel good after a long day at work? Try this facial recipe.

INGREDIENTS

1 tablespoon full-fat yogurt
1 tablespoon cucumber; chopped
1 tablespoon fresh parsley; chopped
3 capsules vitamin E

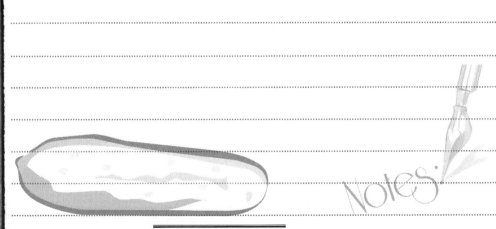

Notes:

Homemade Facial Masks

1 Combine yogurt, cucumber and parsley in blender or food processor and puree.

2 Prick or cut end from vitamin E capsules and squeeze contents into cucumber puree; mix well.

3 Apply evenly to face and neck.

4 Leave on for 15 minutes; relax; rinse with warm water and pat dry.

Soothing Mask

Try this mask to soothe irritated or sunburned skin.

INGREDIENTS

1 tablespoon plain, full-fat yogurt
½ tablespoon dry oatmeal
2 drops jasmine essential oil

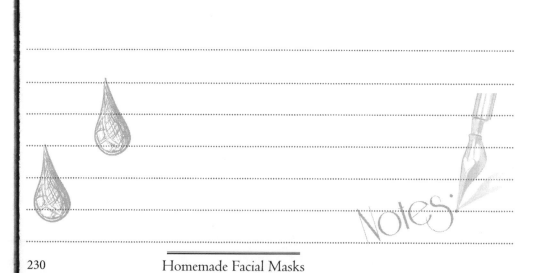

Notes:

1 In a small bowl, combine yogurt and oatmeal; mix well.

2 Add jasmine essential oil.

3 Apply to skin and neck, relax, and leave on for 10 minutes.

4 Rinse with warm water and pat dry.

Strawberries & Dream

A great mask of strawberries and cream that you can use every week to brighten up your skin.

INGREDIENTS

4-5 ripe strawberries
2 teaspoons heavy cream
1 teaspoon honey
½ teaspoon lemon juice
3 capsules vitamin E

Notes:

1 Puree strawberries, cream, lemon and honey together in a blender or food processor.

2 Prick or cut end from vitamin E capsules and squeeze contents into mix; stir well.

3 Apply evenly to face and neck, avoiding area around the eyes.

 4 Leave it on for 10 minutes; relax; rinse with warm water and pat dry.

Toning Up

This mask will leave your skin feeling
firm and toned.

INGREDIENTS

1 egg white
1 strawberry
1 tablespoon starch
3 tablespoons rosewater
2 drops lavender essential oil
1 tablespoon yogurt

Notes:

1 In medium bowl, combine
egg white, strawberry,
starch and rosewater.

2 Add lavender essential
oil and yogurt; mix well.

3 Apply evenly to face and
neck with facial brush; relax
and leave on for 15 minutes.

4 Rinse with warm
water and pat dry.

Cooling Yogurt

A simple soothing mask which is great for sunburned skin.

INGREDIENTS

1 tablespoon plain, full-fat yogurt
1 teaspoon honey, warm
  Optional: For dry skin, use extra
  teaspoon of honey.
  Optional: For oily skin, add a few
  drops of fresh lemon or lime juice.

Notes:

1 Combine yogurt and honey in small bowl and mix well.

2 Apply evenly to face and neck with facial brush.

 3 Relax and leave on for 25 minutes; rinse with warm water and pat dry.

Cat Whispers

This is another recipe that originally called for kitty litter (only the 100% natural clay, unscented, non-clumping type, of course). Remember, the stuff is simply bentonite clay, the same ingredient many high-end spas use to make their special muds and clays for face and body treatments. You can still use the kitty litter if you're feeling adventurous (if you do, please go back and review the "Clays & Kitty Litter" section earlier in the book). So the recipe now calls simply for cosmetic clay of choice. Use green clay for oily skin, white clay for dry, sensitive skin or pink clay for a cleansing but gentle mask.

INGREDIENTS

2 tablespoons cosmetic clay
   of choice
2 tablespoons warm water
2 drops lavender essential oil
1 tablespoon yogurt

Notes:

1 Place cosmetic clay in small bowl; stir in water a bit at a time until a paste is made.

2 Add lavender essential oil and yogurt; mix into paste.

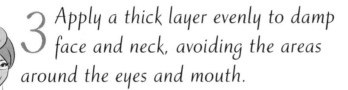

3 Apply a thick layer evenly to damp face and neck, avoiding the areas around the eyes and mouth.

4 Leave mask on for 10-15 minutes, but do not allow the mask to dry. Spritz with water as need to prevent drying.

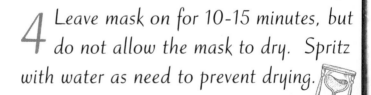

5 Rinse with warm water and pat dry

Crystal Clarity

Clear your mind as you deeply cleanse your skin
with the Crystal Clarity mask.

INGREDIENTS

2 tablespoons green clay
2 tablespoons warm water
2 drops rosewood essential oil
2 drops lavender essential oil
1 teaspoon honey
½ teaspoon lemon juice

Notes:

1 Place green clay in small bowl; stir in water a bit at a time until a paste is made.

2 Add rosewood and lavender essential oils, honey, and lemon juice, and mix into paste.

3 Apply a thick layer evenly to damp face and neck, avoiding the areas around the eyes and mouth.

 4 Leave mask on for 10-15 minutes, but do not allow the mask to dry. Spritz with water as need to prevent drying.

5 Rinse with warm water and pat dry.

Green Tranquility

Here is a great clay mask made with aloe for soothing along with deep cleaning.

INGREDIENTS

2 tablespoons cosmetic clay of choice
1 tablespoon aloe vera gel (fresh from
    the plant is best)
2 tablespoons warm distilled water
2 drops lavender essential oil
1 tablespoon yogurt

1 In a medium bowl blend together aloe vera gel and clay.

2 Add water and continue mixing into a mud/paste.

3 Add lavender essential oil and yogurt; mix into paste.

4 Apply a thick layer evenly to damp face and neck, avoiding the areas around the eyes and mouth.

5 Relax and leave mask on for 10-15 minutes, but do not allow the mask to dry. Spritz with water as needed to prevent drying.

6 Rinse with warm water and pat dry.

Lullaby Facial

Try this clay mask before bedtime; you just might drift away with the heavenly aroma of these essential oils.

INGREDIENTS

2 tablespoons cosmetic clay of choice
2 tablespoons warm distilled water
3 drops lavender essential oil
2 drops chamomile essential oil
1 teaspoon honey
½ teaspoon lemon juice
3 capsules vitamin E

1 In a small bowl, combine clay and essential oils of lavender and chamomile.

2 Add water and mix into a thick mud/paste.

3 Add honey, lemon juice and vitamin E; fold into the paste and mix well

4 Apply a thick layer of the facial evenly to damp face and neck, avoiding the areas around the eyes and mouth.

5 Relax and leave mask on for 10-15 minutes, but do not allow the mask to dry. Spritz with water as need to prevent drying.

6 Rinse with warm water and pat dry.

Pretty in Pink

Pink clay is both cleansing and gentle as it consists of both red clay and white (or kaolin) clay (for more information, refer to the "Clays and Kitty Litter" section earlier in the book).

INGREDIENTS

1½ tablespoons red clay
½ tablespoon white clay
1½ tablespoon fresh aloe vera
1 tablespoon rosewater
2 drops rosewood essential oil
1 tablespoon yogurt

Notes:

1 In a medium size bowl, stir the red and white clays together; add aloe vera (fresh from the plant itself is best), yogurt, rosewater and rosewood essential oil and mix.

 2 Apply a thick layer of the facial evenly to damp face and neck, avoiding the areas around the eyes and mouth.

 3 Relax and leave mask on for 10-15 minutes, but do not allow the mask to fully dry. Spritz with water as needed to prevent drying.

4 Rinse with warm water and pat dry.

For Deep Cleaning

Revitalizing Mix

Reclaim a healthy glow. This recipe is great for
dull and tired skin that could use a boost.

INGREDIENTS

2 tablespoons cosmetic clay of choice
3 tablespoons warm water
1 teaspoon vegetable glycerin
2 drops sweet orange essential oil
2 drops rosewood essential oil

Notes:

1 Combine clay and water in a medium size bowl and mix to a thick paste.

2 Add glycerin, sweet orange essential oil, rosewood essential oil and mix into the paste.

3 Apply a nice thick layer evenly to damp face and neck, avoiding the areas around your eyes and mouth.

4 Relax and leave mask on for 10-15 minutes, but do not allow the mask to dry. Spritz with water as needed to prevent drying.

5 Rinse with warm water and pat dry.

Morning Dew

Here's a great mask for young men and
women in their teens and 20s.

INGREDIENTS

1 tablespoon brewer's yeast
½ cup plain, full-fat yogurt
1 tablespoon honey

Notes:

Homemade Facial Masks

1 In a small bowl, combine yeast and yogurt; stir well and store in the refrigerator overnight.

2 Add honey and mix well.

3 Apply heavy layer to face and neck, avoiding the area around the eyes.

4 Relax with mask on for 25 minutes; rinse with warm water and pat dry.

Refresh & Revive

As we age, our skin changes. We don't even think about it until that day we start noticing something is different. Try this refreshing mixture and your skin will look and feel revived!

INGREDIENTS

2 tablespoons organic coconut oil
1 egg yolk
1 tablespoon honey
1 tablespoon plain, full-fat yogurt
1 teaspoon table sugar

Notes:

1 Place yogurt, egg yolk, honey, coconut oil and sugar in bowl or a blender and mix well.

2 Apply evenly to your face and neck, avoiding the eyes.

PrettySmart Tip

Lots of people love coconut oil on their face (and it makes a fabulous hair conditioner, too!), but coconut oil can be comedogenic, meaning it can clog your pores and could lead your skin to break out if you are at all prone to acne. If you have sensitive or acne-prone skin, instead of coconut, substitute an equal amount of non-comedogenic oil like jojoba, borage or meadowfoam oil.

3 Relax and enjoy your mask for 20 minutes; rinse with warm water and pat dry.

The Ages

Nurture and Renew

In our 40s, our skin typically begins to loose elasticity. Try this recipe for a mask that is sure to nurture and renew your skin.

INGREDIENTS

2 tablespoons sweet peas
1 tablespoon almond oil
¼ cup carrot juice
2 drops lavender essential oil
1 tablespoon plain, full-fat yogurt

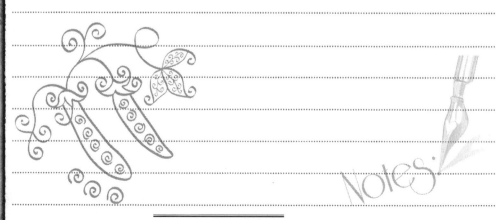

Notes:

Homemade Facial Masks

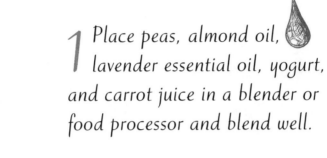

1 Place peas, almond oil, lavender essential oil, yogurt, and carrot juice in a blender or food processor and blend well.

2 Apply mixture to face and neck, avoiding the area around the eyes.

3 Relax with mask in place for 30 minutes; rinse with warm water and pat dry.

Elegance & Wisdom

For those of us 50 and better, we know how important skin care is. This mask is rich in antioxidants and other healthy ingredients to pamper and support your skin. Find these powders at your local health food store and enjoy your time with you.

INGREDIENTS

1 teaspoon green tea powder
1 teaspoon goji berry powder
1 teaspoon açaí berry powder
1 teaspoon pomegranate juice powder
1 teaspoon grape seed extract
1 tablespoon wheat germ oil
1 tablespoon evening primrose oil
1 tablespoon pure glycerin

Notes:

1 In a small bowl, combine all dry ingredients — tea powder, goji and açaí berry powder, pomegranate juice powder and grape seed extract.

2 In a medium size bowl, combine wheat germ oil, evening primrose oil and glycerin.

3 Add dried ingredients to oil blend using a spatula to blend well.

4 Using a facial brush, apply generous layer to the face and neck; relax and let sit for 25 minutes.

5 Rinse with warm water and pat dry.

Face Mask Journal

Mask Name: .... Date: ....

Rating:　10　9　8　7　6　5　4　3　2　1　Page Number: ....

Thoughts: ....

....

....

....

....

....

....

Sensitivities or adverse reactions (note particular ingredients and level of reaction, if any):

When I use this mask, I notice...

☐　Improvement in skin color and clarity

☐　Improved skin texture and hydration

☐　Skin tone more balanced (not as dry; not as oily)

☐　I feel more open, relaxed and refreshed

☐　I'm glad I took the time to care for my body, mind and spirit

Face Mask Journal

Mask Name:

Date:

Rating: 10 9 8 7 6 5 4 3 2 1

Page Number:

Thoughts:

....

....

....

....

....

....

When I use this mask, I notice...

☐   Improvement in skin color and clarity

☐   Improved skin texture and hydration

☐   Skin tone more balanced (not as dry; not as oily)

☐   I feel more open, relaxed and refreshed

☐   I'm glad I took the time to care for my body, mind and spirit

Sensitivities or adverse reactions (note particular ingredients and level of reaction, if any):

Face Mask Journal

Mask Name: _____ Date: _____

Rating: 10 9 8 7 6 5 4 3 2 1   Page Number: _____

Thoughts: _____

_____

_____

_____

_____

_____

Sensitivities or adverse reactions (note particular ingredients and level of reaction, if any):

When I use this mask, I notice...

☐ Improvement in skin color and clarity

☐ Improved skin texture and hydration

☐ Skin tone more balanced (not as dry; not as oily)

☐ I feel more open, relaxed and refreshed

☐ I'm glad I took the time to care for my body, mind and spirit

Face Mask Journal

Mask Name: .... Date: ....

Rating: 10 9 8 7 6 5 4 3 2 1 Page Number: ....

Thoughts: ....

....

....

....

....

....

....

When I use this mask, I notice...

☐ Improvement in skin color and clarity

☐ Improved skin texture and hydration

☐ Skin tone more balanced (not as dry; not as oily)

☐ I feel more open, relaxed and refreshed

☐ I'm glad I took the time to care for my body, mind and spirit

Sensitivities or adverse reactions (note particular ingredients and level of reaction, if any):

Face Mask Journal

Mask Name: .... Date: ....

Rating: 10 9 8 7 6 5 4 3 2 1   Page Number: ....

Thoughts: ....

....

....

....

....

....

....

Sensitivities or adverse reactions (note particular ingredients and level of reaction, if any):

When I use this mask, I notice...

☐   Improvement in skin color and clarity

☐   Improved skin texture and hydration

☐   Skin tone more balanced (not as dry; not as oily)

☐   I feel more open, relaxed and refreshed

☐   I'm glad I took the time to care for my body, mind and spirit

Face Mask Journal

Mask Name: .... Date: ....

Rating: 10 9 8 7 6 5 4 3 2 1   Page Number: ....

Thoughts: ....

....

....

....

....

....

....

When I use this mask, I notice...

Sensitivities or adverse reactions (note particular ingredients and level of reaction, if any):

☐ Improvement in skin color and clarity

☐ Improved skin texture and hydration

☐ Skin tone more balanced (not as dry; not as oily)

☐ I feel more open, relaxed and refreshed

☐ I'm glad I took the time to care for my body, mind and spirit

Face Mask Journal

Mask Name: .... Date: ....

Rating: 10   9   8   7   6   5   4   3   2   1   Page Number: ....

Thoughts: ....

....

....

....

....

....

....

When I use this mask, I notice...

Sensitivities or adverse reactions (note particular ingredients and level of reaction, if any):

☐   Improvement in skin color and clarity

☐   Improved skin texture and hydration

☐   Skin tone more balanced (not as dry; not as oily)

☐   I feel more open, relaxed and refreshed

☐   I'm glad I took the time to care for my body, mind and spirit

Face Mask Journal

Mask Name: ....

Date: ....

Rating: 10 9 8 7 6 5 4 3 2 1

Page Number: ....

Thoughts: ....

....

....

....

....

....

....

Sensitivities or adverse reactions (note particular ingredients and level of reaction, if any):

When I use this mask, I notice...

☐ Improvement in skin color and clarity

☐ Improved skin texture and hydration

☐ Skin tone more balanced (not as dry; not as oily)

☐ I feel more open, relaxed and refreshed

☐ I'm glad I took the time to care for my body, mind and spirit

Face Mask Journal

Mask Name: .... Date: ....

Rating: 10   9   8   7   6   5   4   3   2   1   Page Number: ....

Thoughts: ....

....

....

....

....

....

....

When I use this mask, I notice...

☐   *Improvement in skin color and clarity*

☐   *Improved skin texture and hydration*

☐   *Skin tone more balanced (not as dry; not as oily)*

☐   *I feel more open, relaxed and refreshed*

☐   *I'm glad I took the time to care for my body, mind and spirit*

Sensitivities or adverse reactions (note particular ingredients and level of reaction, if any):

Face Mask Journal

Mask Name: .... Date: ....

Rating: 10   9   8   7   6   5   4   3   2   1   Page Number: ....

Thoughts: ....

....

....

....

....

....

When I use this mask, I notice...

☐ Improvement in skin color and clarity

☐ Improved skin texture and hydration

☐ Skin tone more balanced (not as dry; not as oily)

☐ I feel more open, relaxed and refreshed

☐ I'm glad I took the time to care for my body, mind and spirit

Sensitivities or adverse reactions (note particular ingredients and level of reaction, if any):

Face Mask Journal

Mask Name: Date:

Rating: 10 9 8 7 6 5 4 3 2 1   Page Number:

Thoughts:

....

....

....

....

....

....

....

Sensitivities or adverse reactions (note particular ingredients and level of reaction, if any):

When I use this mask, I notice...

- ☐ Improvement in skin color and clarity
- ☐ Improved skin texture and hydration
- ☐ Skin tone more balanced (not as dry; not as oily)
- ☐ I feel more open, relaxed and refreshed
- ☐ I'm glad I took the time to care for my body, mind and spirit

Face Mask Journal

Mask Name: Date:

Rating: 10 9 8 7 6 5 4 3 2 1   Page Number:

Thoughts:

....

....

....

....

....

....

When I use this mask, I notice...

☐   Improvement in skin color and clarity

☐   Improved skin texture and hydration

☐   Skin tone more balanced (not as dry; not as oily)

☐   I feel more open, relaxed and refreshed

☐   I'm glad I took the time to care for my body, mind and spirit

Sensitivities or adverse reactions (note particular ingredients and level of reaction, if any):

Face Mask Journal

Mask Name: Date:

Rating: 10   9   8   7   6   5   4   3   2   1   Page Number:

Thoughts:

....

....

....

....

....

Sensitivities or adverse reactions (note particular ingredients and level of reaction, if any):

When I use this mask, I notice...

☐ Improvement in skin color and clarity

☐ Improved skin texture and hydration

☐ Skin tone more balanced (not as dry; not as oily)

☐ I feel more open, relaxed and refreshed

☐ I'm glad I took the time to care for my body, mind and spirit

Face Mask Journal

Mask Name: .... Date: ....

Rating: 10 9 8 7 6 5 4 3 2 1   Page Number: ....

Thoughts: ....

....

....

....

....

....

....

Sensitivities or adverse reactions (note particular ingredients and level of reaction, if any):

When I use this mask, I notice...

☐ Improvement in skin color and clarity

☐ Improved skin texture and hydration

☐ Skin tone more balanced (not as dry; not as oily)

☐ I feel more open, relaxed and refreshed

☐ I'm glad I took the time to care for my body, mind and spirit

Face Mask Journal

Mask Name: .... Date: ....

Rating: 10 9 8 7 6 5 4 3 2 1   Page Number: ....

Thoughts: ....

....

....

....

....

....

....

Sensitivities or adverse reactions (note particular ingredients and level of reaction, if any):

When I use this mask, I notice...

☐ Improvement in skin color and clarity

☐ Improved skin texture and hydration

☐ Skin tone more balanced (not as dry; not as oily)

☐ I feel more open, relaxed and refreshed

☐ I'm glad I took the time to care for my body, mind and spirit

Face Mask Journal

Mask Name: .... Date: ....

Rating: 10 9 8 7 6 5 4 3 2 1   Page Number: ....

Thoughts: ....

....

....

....

....

....

....

When I use this mask, I notice...

☐ Improvement in skin color and clarity

☐ Improved skin texture and hydration

Sensitivities or adverse reactions (note particular ingredients and level of reaction, if any):

☐ Skin tone more balanced (not as dry; not as oily)

☐ I feel more open, relaxed and refreshed

☐ I'm glad I took the time to care for my body, mind and spirit

Face Mask Journal

Mask Name: .... Date: ....

Rating: 10 9 8 7 6 5 4 3 2 1   Page Number: ....

Thoughts: ....

....

....

....

....

....

....

When I use this mask, I notice...

☐   Improvement in skin color and clarity

☐   Improved skin texture and hydration

☐   Skin tone more balanced (not as dry; not as oily)

☐   I feel more open, relaxed and refreshed

☐   I'm glad I took the time to care for my body, mind and spirit

Sensitivities or adverse reactions (note particular ingredients and level of reaction, if any):

Face Mask Journal

Mask Name: Date:

Rating: 10 9 8 7 6 5 4 3 2 1   Page Number:

Thoughts:

Sensitivities or adverse reactions (note particular ingredients and level of reaction, if any):

When I use this mask, I notice...

☐   Improvement in skin color and clarity

☐   Improved skin texture and hydration

☐   Skin tone more balanced (not as dry; not as oily)

☐   I feel more open, relaxed and refreshed

☐   I'm glad I took the time to care for my body, mind and spirit

Face Mask Journal

Mask Name: _____ Date: _____

Rating: 10 9 8 7 6 5 4 3 2 1   Page Number: _____

Thoughts: _____

_____

_____

_____

_____

_____

_____

When I use this mask, I notice...

☐ Improvement in skin color and clarity

☐ Improved skin texture and hydration

☐ Skin tone more balanced (not as dry; not as oily)

☐ I feel more open, relaxed and refreshed

☐ I'm glad I took the time to care for my body, mind and spirit

Sensitivities or adverse reactions (note particular ingredients and level of reaction, if any):

Face Mask Journal

Mask Name: ....   Date: ....

Rating: 10   9   8   7   6   5   4   3   2   1   Page Number: ....

Thoughts: ....

....

....

....

....

....

....

When I use this mask, I notice...

☐   Improvement in skin color and clarity

☐   Improved skin texture and hydration

☐   Skin tone more balanced (not as dry; not as oily)

☐   I feel more open, relaxed and refreshed

☐   I'm glad I took the time to care for my body, mind and spirit

Sensitivities or adverse reactions (note particular ingredients and level of reaction, if any):

Index

W

Y

Made in the USA
San Bernardino, CA
22 December 2013